ECOLOGY & THE ENVIRONMENT - BIG BOOK

Ecology & The Environment

Written by Angela Wagner

GRADES 5 - 8

Reading Levels 3 - 4

Classroom Complete Press
P.O. Box 19729
San Diego, CA 92159
Tel: 1-800-663-3609 | Fax: 1-800-663-3608
Email: service@classroomcompletepress.com

www.classroomcompletepress.com

ISBN-13: 978-1-5539-369-2
ISBN-10: 1-55319-369-5

Critical Thinking Skills

Ecology & the Environment

Ecosystems
Classification & Adaptation
Cells
Ecology & the Environment - Big Book

Level	Skills For Critical Thinking	Reading Comprehension: Section 1	Section 2	Section 3	Section 4	Section 5	Section 6	Section 7	Section 8	Hands-On Activities
LEVEL 1 Knowledge	• List Details/Facts	✓	✓	✓	✓	✓	✓	✓	✓	✓
	• Recall Information	✓	✓	✓	✓	✓	✓	✓	✓	✓
	• Match Vocab to Definitions	✓	✓	✓	✓	✓	✓	✓	✓	
	• Define Vocabulary	✓	✓	✓	✓	✓		✓	✓	
	• Label Diagrams		✓		✓	✓		✓		✓
	• Recognize Validity (T/F)	✓	✓	✓	✓	✓	✓	✓	✓	
LEVEL 2 Comprehension	• Demonstrate Understanding	✓	✓	✓	✓	✓	✓	✓	✓	✓
	• Explain Scientific Causation		✓	✓			✓			
	• Rephrasing Vocab Meaning	✓	✓	✓	✓	✓		✓	✓	
	• Describe	✓				✓	✓	✓		✓
	• Classify into Scientific Groups		✓		✓	✓	✓		✓	
LEVEL 3 Application	• Application to Own Life	✓		✓	✓	✓	✓	✓	✓	✓
	• Model Scientific Process			✓		✓			✓	
	• Organize & Classify Facts	✓		✓	✓				✓	✓
	• Use Alternative Research Tools	✓	✓	✓	✓	✓	✓	✓	✓	✓
LEVEL 4 Analysis	• Distinguish Roles/Meanings	✓	✓		✓	✓		✓	✓	
	• Make Inferences	✓	✓	✓		✓	✓			✓
	• Draw Conclusions Based on Facts Provided	✓	✓	✓	✓	✓	✓	✓	✓	✓
	• Classify Based on Facts Researched	✓	✓	✓			✓			
LEVEL 5 Synthesis	• Compile Research Information	✓	✓	✓	✓	✓	✓	✓	✓	
	• Design & Application	✓	✓	✓	✓	✓	✓	✓	✓	✓
	• Create & Construct	✓	✓	✓	✓	✓	✓	✓	✓	
	• Imagine Self in Scientific Role	✓	✓	✓	✓	✓	✓	✓	✓	✓
LEVEL 6 Evaluation	• State & Defend an Opinion		✓		✓		✓		✓	
	• Justify Choices for Research Topics	✓	✓	✓	✓	✓	✓	✓	✓	
	• Defend Selections & Reasoning			✓	✓				✓	✓

Based on Bloom's Taxonomy

Contents

TEACHER GUIDE

STUDENT HANDOUTS

Contents

Cells

FREE!

✔ **18 BONUS Activity Pages! Additional worksheets for your students**

- Go to our website: **www.classroomcompletepress.com/bonus**
- Enter item CC4500 or Ecosystems
- Enter pass code CC4500D for Activity Pages.

- Enter item CC4501 or Classification & Adaptation
- Enter pass code CC4501D for Activity Pages.

- Enter item CC4502 or Cells
- Enter pass code CC4502D for Activity Pages.

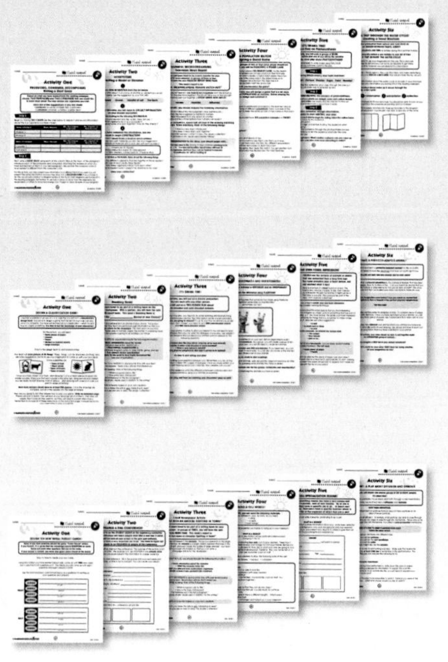

Assessment Rubric

Ecology & the Environment

Student's Name: ____________ Assignment: ____________ Level: ________

	Level 1	Level 2	Level 3	Level 4
Understanding Concepts	Demonstrates a limited understanding of concepts. Requires teacher intervention	Demonstrates a basic understanding of concepts. Requires little teacher intervention	Demonstrates a good understanding of concepts. Requires no teacher intervention	Demonstrates a thorough understanding of concepts. Requires no teacher intervention
Analysis and Application of Key Concepts	Limited application and interpretation in activity responses	Basic application and interpretation in activity responses	Good application and interpretation in activity responses	Strong application and interpretation in activity responses
Creativity and Imagination	Limited creativity and imagination applied in projects and activities	Some creativity and imagination applied in projects and activities	Satisfactory level of creativity and imagination applied in projects and activities	Beyond expected creativity and imagination applied in projects & activities
Application of Own Interests	Limited application of own interests in independent or group environment	Basic application of own interests in independent or group environment	Good application of own interests in independent or group environment	Strong application of own interests in independent or group environment

STRENGTHS:

WEAKNESSES:

NEXT STEPS:

Teacher Guide

Our resource has been created for ease of use by both TEACHERS and STUDENTS alike.

Introduction

This resource provides ready-to-use information and activities for remedial students in grades five to eight. Written to grade and using simplified language and vocabulary, science concepts are presented in a way that makes them more accessible to students and easier to understand. Comprised of reading passages, student activities and mini posters, our resource can be used effectively for whole-class, small group and independent work.

How Is Our Resource Organized?

STUDENT HANDOUTS

Reading passages and **activities** (*in the form of reproducible worksheets*) make up the majority of our resource. The reading passages present important grade-appropriate information and concepts related to the topic. Embedded in each passage are one or more questions that ensure students understand what they have read.

For each reading passage there are **BEFORE YOU READ** activities and **AFTER YOU READ** activities. As with the reading passages, the related activities are written using a remedial level of language.

- The BEFORE YOU READ activities prepare students for reading by setting a purpose for reading. They stimulate background knowledge and experience, and guide students to make connections between what they know and what they will learn. Important concepts and vocabulary from the chapters are also presented.
- The AFTER YOU READ activities check students' comprehension of the concepts presented in the reading passage and extend their learning. Students are asked to give thoughtful consideration of the reading passage through creative and evaluative short-answer questions, research, and extension activities.

Hands-on activities are included to further develop students' thinking skills and understanding of the concepts. The **Assessment Rubric** (*page 5*) is a useful tool for evaluating students' responses to many of the activities in our resource. The **Comprehension Quiz** (*page 50*) can be used for either a follow-up review or assessment at the completion of the unit.

PICTURE CUES

This resource contains three main types of pages, each with a different purpose and use. A **Picture Cue** at the top of each page shows, at a glance, what the page is for.

Teacher Guide
- Information and tools for the teacher

Student Handout
- Reproducible worksheets and activities

Easy Marking™ Answer Key
- Answers for student activities

EASY MARKING™ ANSWER KEY

Marking students' worksheets is fast and easy with this **Answer Key**. Answers are listed in columns – just line up the column with its corresponding worksheet, as shown, and see how every question matches up with its answer!

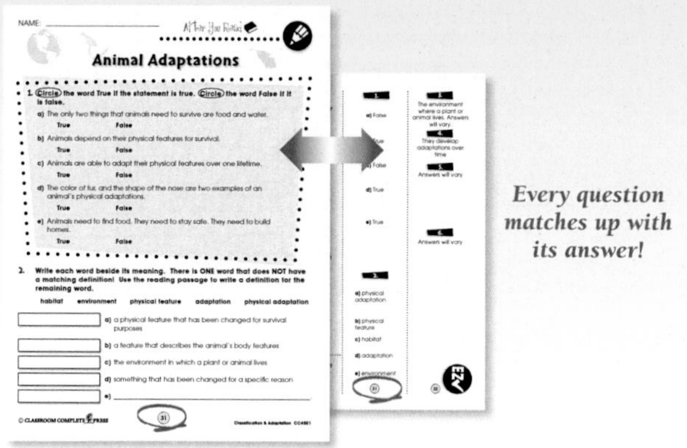

Every question matches up with its answer!

Bloom's Taxonomy

***Our resource is an effective tool for any* SCIENCE PROGRAM.**

Bloom's Taxonomy* for Reading Comprehension

The activities in our resource engage and build the full range of thinking skills that are essential for students' reading comprehension and understanding of important geography concepts. Based on the six levels of thinking in Bloom's Taxonomy, and using language at a remedial level, information and questions are given that challenge students to not only recall what they have read, but move beyond this to understand the text and concepts through higher-order thinking. By using higher-order skills of application, analysis, synthesis and evaluation, students become active readers, drawing more meaning from the text, attaining a greater understanding of concepts, and applying and extending their learning in more sophisticated ways.

Our resource, therefore, is an effective tool for any Science program. Whether it is used in whole or in part, or adapted to meet individual student needs, our resource provides teachers with essential information and questions to ask, inspiring students' interest, creativity, and promoting meaningful learning.

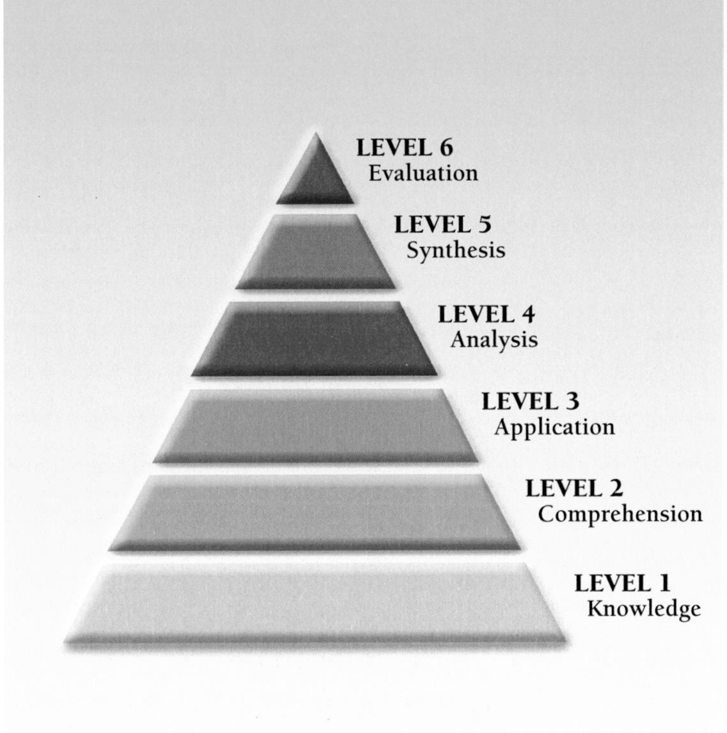

BLOOM'S TAXONOMY:
6 LEVELS OF THINKING

***Bloom's Taxonomy is a widely used tool by educators for classifying learning objectives, and is based on the work of Benjamin Bloom.**

Vocabulary

Ecosystems
Classification & Adaptation
Cells
Ecology & the Environment - Big Book

• ecosystem • matter • classification • cell • biotic • senses • magnify
• abiotic • microscope • vertebrae • system • building block • biologist
• amoeba • solar energy • environment • multicellular • balance
• cold-blooded • organism • reproduce • category • single-celled
• population • nucleus • kingdom • DNA • cell membrane • interbreed
• phylum • cytoplasm • class • succession • family • composition
• species • producer • warm-blooded • cilia • consumer • organelle
• invertebrate • particles • vertebrate • decomposer • recycle
• food web • nerve • food chain • tissue • interaction
• cell specialization • fossil • nutrients • specialize • insect
• sugar • oxygen • chromosome • mollusk • mitosis • photosynthesis
• meiosis • arachnid • asexual reproduction • carbon dioxide
• cell wall • symmetrical • vacuole • leaves • habitat • energy
• physical feature • centriole • water cycle • adaptation • evaporation
• paleontologist • plastid • collection • lysosome • physical adaptation
• tissue • precipitation • organ • marsupial • condensation
• organ system • climate • microscope • diffusion • opposable thumb
• osmosis • virus • active transport • bacteria • evolution
• passive transport • microorganism • sedimentary rock
• semi-permeable • fungi

NAME: ______________________________

Ecosystems

1. Fill in the blanks using a word from the list below. You may use a dictionary to help.

system environment balance ecosystem biotic abiotic

a) The word [ ] describes a group of things that work and live together in an environment.

b) Something that is living is described as being [ ].

c) A [ ] is when all parts of a system work and live happily together.

d) A group of things that work together is called a [ ].

e) When something is not living, for example a rock, it is called [ ].

f) The whole area surrounding someone or something is called their [ ].

2. List <u>FIVE</u> things that live in each of these places:

Rainforest	Puddle	Handful of Soil	Planet Earth
________	________	________	________
________	________	________	________
________	________	________	________
________	________	________	________
________	________	________	________

3. Imagine you are stranded in the middle of a desert. Describe two living things and two non-living things that you might find there.

____

____

NAME: ______________________

Ecosystems

What Is an Ecosystem?

an you find two words in the bigger word, **"ECOSYSTEM"**? "Eco" means life forms and the environment in which they live. A "system" is a group of things that work together. Now put the two words back together.

An **ecosystem** is a group of things that work and live together in an environment. An example of an ecosystem is a rainforest, a pond, a city or even our Earth!

What Is an Ecosystem Made Of?

Everything we see can be put into two groups. If you look around, you will see both **biotic** and **abiotic** things. **Biotic** describes something that is living or was once alive. **Biotic** things include frogs, leaves, dead trees and humans. **Abiotic** means everything else that is not living. **Abiotic** things include rocks, cars, computers, and gold.

Describe your own example of an ecosystem. What BIOTIC and ABIOTIC things would you find in your ecosystem?

____

____

How Big is an Ecosystem?

Ecosystems can be as big as a planet. They can also be as small as a puddle! Plants and animals live in ecosystems. Things that are too small to see also live in ecosystems. Everywhere you look, you can find an ecosystem.

Even a handful of soil is an ecosystem. There are many things living in soil. You may think that soil is just dirt. If you looked closely, you would find worms, bugs, sand and many more things. They are all part of the soil's ecosystem.

All parts of an ecosystem work and live together. They are just like people who live in the same neighborhood or city. Humans have jobs and so do things in an ecosystem. They need to work together to live and be happy. This makes the ecosystem balanced. Without a balance, the ecosystem will not work!

Ecosystems

1. Draw a straight line from the word on the left to its definition on the right. Which word is left over? Use the reading passage or a dictionary to help you write out its definition.

1	system	Describes something that is not living, for example, a computer	A
2	biotic	Looks at life forms and the environment where they live	B
3	ecosystem	A group of things that work together	C
4	eco	Describes something that is living, for example, a frog	D
5	abiotic	______________________ ______________________	E

2. Circle T if the statement is TRUE or F if it is FALSE. If it is false, rewrite the sentence to make it true.

T F a) Everything we see around us is living.

____

T F b) An ecosystem only works if there is a balance and all parts work and live together.

____

T F c) A desert, a puddle, a jungle and our planet Earth are all examples of ecosystems.

____

T F d) A handful of soil is too small to be called an ecosystem.

____

T F e) A dead tree is an example of an abiotic thing.

____

After You Read

NAME: ____________________

Ecosystems

3. In what ways could your classroom be described as an ecosystem? Name two **abiotic** and two **biotic** things in your classroom.

____

____

4. Are all **ecosystems** the same size? Use examples to explain your answer.

____

____

Extension & Application

5. **Imagine you are a frog living somewhere in the world.** Use both your imagination and research tools to come up with facts about the ecosystem in which you live.

Copy the chart below onto a separate piece of paper to help you organize your thoughts and facts.

	Imagination	Research Tools
Where they live (i.e., water, soil)		
What they need to survive		
Biotic things found in their ecosystem		
Other abiotic things found in their ecosystem		

6. **TRAVEL TO AN ECOSYSTEM!** Design a **travel poster** which will convince people to come visit this ecosystem. Choose any ecosystem (try to think of one not yet mentioned) and use pictures and words to describe what you would find in this ecosystem. Remember… an ecosystem doesn't have to be a big place, and it has both biotic and abiotic things in it!

In your poster, be sure to include:

- The name of your ecosystem (a title)
- A slogan or sentence convincing people to come visit
- Drawings of both living and non-living things
- Research facts about the different parts of the ecosystem

NAME: ______________________

Populations

1. Draw a straight line from the word on the left to its definition on the right. You may use a dictionary to help.

1	organism	A group of similar individuals living in the same geographic area	A
2	reproduce	To produce offspring or children which increases a population	B
3	population	A group of things that live and work together in the same environment	C
4	interbreed	A living thing such as a plant or animal	D
5	ecosystem	To reproduce with another organism within the same population	E

2. Use a dictionary to look up the word INTERACTION. Write the definition below.

The dictionary definition of an **interaction** is:

____

____

3. Think about the last **interaction** you had with someone before you started this activity. Describe who the interaction was between. Then come up with your own definition of an **interaction**.

____

____

____

____

Reading Passage

NAME: ______________________

Populations

Let us go back and remind ourselves what an **ecosystem** is. We can remember that it is made up of small groups of things that interact with each other. They interact with each other in an environment. What do we mean by these "things'? These interacting things are called organisms. An **organism** is any individual form of life. An example of an organism is a plant or an animal.

An organism cannot live or interact by itself. It needs another organism in its ecosystem to interact with. Since many organisms live in an ecosystem, there will be many organisms that are similar. We call this group of similar organisms a population. A **population** is a group of similar individuals living in the same geographic area. For example, a field full of sunflowers next to a field where there are no sunflowers is a population. An area of water that contains many killer whales is also an example of a population.

Can you think of another example of a population?

____

____

____

It is important to remember two things about populations. First, these individual organisms need to be similar. To be similar, they need to look similar, eat similar food, move in a similar way, and so on. Second, they need to live in the same area. A killer whale that lives in one ocean is not part of the same population as a killer whale that lives in another ocean.

Populations

For example, there are many killer whales that live on our planet. A killer whale population would only include whales that live together and interbreed. If they do not, they are not part of the same population.

How Do Populations Grow?

All populations change over time. Populations may grow or they may shrink. We know that human populations grow. So do populations of things other than humans. They grow because organisms in the same population **interbreed**. This means that organisms only **reproduce** with other organisms in the same population. When organisms **reproduce**, the number of organisms in a population increases.

Explain why the population in the city you live in might get bigger or smaller.

____

____

It is important to remember two things about populations. First, these individual organisms need to be similar. To be similar, they need to look similar, eat similar food, move in a similar way, and so on. Second, they need to live in the same area. A killer whale that lives in one ocean is not part of the same population as a killer whale that lives in another ocean.

After You Read

NAME: ______________________

Populations

1. Put a check mark (✓) next to the answer that best finishes the sen-

a) An ecosystem is made up of a small group of things that...

- ◯ **A** have never seen each other before.
- ◯ **B** interact with each other.
- ◯ **C** all live in different parts of the world.
- ◯ **D** all look exactly the same.

b) An organism is...

- ◯ **A** anything that is so small you can not see it with your own eyes.
- ◯ **B** an animal that has all the organs that humans have.
- ◯ **C** any individual form of life.
- ◯ **D** a group of things that live and work together in a small environment.

c) A population is a group of similar individuals that...

- ◯ **A** eat different kinds of food.
- ◯ **B** live in different locations but still look similar.
- ◯ **C** do not interact with other individuals in their population.
- ◯ **D** live in the same geographic area.

d) An example of a population is...

- ◯ **A** all the monkeys that live in Earth.
- ◯ **B** a group of Great White sharks that live in the Pacific Ocean.
- ◯ **C** a group of people that live in Florida and another group of people that live in Texas.
- ◯ **D** all colonies of ants that live in different sandy beaches.

2. Circle T if the statement is TRUE or F if it is FALSE.

T F a) It is difficult to find many similar organisms in an ecosystem.

T F b) A population is a group of individuals that are similar but may live in different parts of the world.

T F c) A group of dolphins living in the Pacific Ocean is a good example of a population.

T F d) Populations do not grow because they do not reproduce.

T F e) If the number of organisms in a population goes down, the population can still survive.

NAME: ______________________

Populations

Answer the questions in complete sentences.

3. How does a **population** grow?

____

4. Can it be difficult for a **population** to survive in an **ecosystem**? Explain why or why not.

____

____

Extension & Application

5. Copy and complete the chart below. Come up with an example of a population for the organism on the left side of the chart. Then come up with an example that would not be a good example of a population. The first question has been completed for you.

Organism	Population example	Not a population example
Monkey	All the curly-tailed monkeys that live in South Africa	
Maple tree		
Worm		
Snake		
Daisy flower		

6. CALLING ALL WRITERS AND ARTISTS!
Pick an organism from the list above and complete ONLY ONE of the following projects, either Project A or Project B. If you need help, you can use research tools to find information about your organism. Don't forget to use your imagination too!

Project A: STORY
Write a story about the organism you have chosen to be. Be sure to include the following: introduce who you are, who is part of your population, where you live, and any other information that describes what life is like to be your organism.

Project B: DRAWING
Draw a population picture! Use your imagination to draw a full-page picture showing you (the organism you have chosen) and your population. By looking at your picture you should be able to see: what organism you have chosen, who is part of your population, where you live, and any other details you think are important.

NAME: ____________________

Change in Ecosystems

1. **a)** What does the word **balance** mean to you?

____

____

b) Can you think of situations where balance is **very** important? One line has already been filled for you. Can you think of **four** more?

Balancing on a tightrope in a circus

1 ______________________________

2 ______________________________

3 ______________________________

4 ______________________________

2. Complete each sentence with a word from the list. You may use a dictionary to help.

population succession ecosystems biotic environment composition

a) [ ] describes what happens when something changes over a long period of time.

b) The word that describes a group of things that work and live together in an environment is an [ ].

c) In an ecosystem, you will find abiotic things (non-living things) and [ ] things (living things).

d) The [ ] where someone or something lives includes the whole area surrounding them.

e) The [ ] of a jar of jellybeans includes all the different colors of jellybeans that are in the jar.

f) A group of similar individuals living in the same geographic area is called a [ ].

NAME: ______________________________

Change in Ecosystems

Do Ecosystems Change Over Time?

Everything that lives in our world changes over time. Humans change. Our bodies change. Animals change. Plants change. Every living thing changes over time, including ecosystems. What an ecosystem looks like changes, and so does its composition. The **composition** of an ecosystem describes everything that is part of an ecosystem. This includes both living and non-living things, both biotic and abiotic things.

STOP

Look around you right now. Pick the first thing you see. Describe how it changes over time.

____

____

____

____

When an ecosystem changes over a long period of time, it is called **succession**. The populations in an ecosystem change during succession. A population may become smaller over time. A population may even disappear completely. A population may become much bigger. Something else may happen during succession. Species from ecosystems close by might come and move into the ecosystem. These are all changes that may happen to an ecosystem over time. They are all part of succession.

An ecosystem might also change because of humans. For example, when we develop land for houses, we cut down trees. We change the environment for all plants and animals. Some animals can adapt to the change. Others can not. Their population is then affected.

After You Read

NAME: ______________________

Change in Ecosystems

1. Write the answer that best completes the sentences below.

a) [ ] (**Some** / **Every**) living thing changes over time.

b) Animals and plants change over time. [ ] (**Ecosystems** / **Atmospheres**) also change over time.

c) The [ ] (**energy** / **composition**) of an ecosystem includes both biotic and abiotic things.

d) Populations in an ecosystem [ ] (**change** / **stay the same**) during succession.

e) An ecosystem might change because of natural causes but it may also change because of [ ] (**heavy rain** / **humans**).

2. Circle T if the statement is TRUE or F if it is FALSE.

T F **a)** Humans, animals, and plants change over time but ecosystems do not change over time.

T F **b)** The composition of an ecosystem describes everything that is part of an ecosystem.

T F **c)** When an ecosystem changes over a long period of time, it is called evolution.

T F **d)** During succession, a population may get bigger but it might also disappear completely.

T F **e)** Cutting down trees, building houses, and dumping garbage are all examples of how humans can harmfully affect an ecosystem.

NAME: ______________________

Change in Ecosystems

3. What is the composition of an ecosystem?

____

____

4. How can an ecosystem change over time during **succession**?

____

____

5. Describe how humans can have a large **impact** on an ecosystem. Give at least two examples.

____

____

Extension & Application

6. SAVE OUR ECOSYSTEMS T-shirt Design Contest!

You have already read about how humans can harm an ecosystem. Cutting down trees for houses is one way. Can you think of another one?

You have been entered into a T-shirt design contest. **Your task is to design a T-shirt that shows what humans can do to stop harming our ecosystems.** Pick ONE harmful human activity and use it for your T-shirt design.

Your T-shirt should have:

- a slogan (a sentence telling humans what to stop doing, for example, "Stop Cutting Down Trees!")
- words and pictures that support your slogan

Harmful human activity chosen: ______________________

Slogan on T-shirt: ______________________

Remember, be creative and design a T-shirt that you would like to wear!

NAME: ______________________

T-Shirt Design Contest!

Write "Save Our Ecosystems!" on the line in the shirt

NAME: ______________________________

Producers, Consumers & Decomposers

1. Produce, consume, decompose. What do these words mean? Look up these three words. First, use a dictionary to write down the word's definition. Second, use the word in your own sentence, showing that you understand its meaning.

A produce

Dictionary: ______________________________

Own sentence: ______________________________

B consume

Dictionary: ______________________________

Own sentence: ______________________________

C decompose

Dictionary: ______________________________

Own sentence: ______________________________

2. Complete each sentence with a word from the list. You may use a dictionary to help.

producer   sun   consumer   recycle   decomposer

a) The ________ is the main source of energy for everything on our Earth. It gives off light and heat.

b) ________ are things that break down material in dead organisms.

c) We ________ things so that we can use them again.

d) Something that can make its own food is called a ________.

e) A ________ is something that uses something else to get food and energy.

NAME: ______________________

Producers, Consumers & Decomposers

All organisms in an ecosystem get energy from the same place. All energy comes from the Sun. Green plants absorb this energy. This energy is then shared with all parts of an ecosystem. Every organism in an ecosystem gets their energy and food a different way. This divides all organisms into three kinds: **producers**, **consumers**, and **decomposers**. The difference between these three kinds of organisms is the way they find food and energy. Let us now look at the three different kinds now.

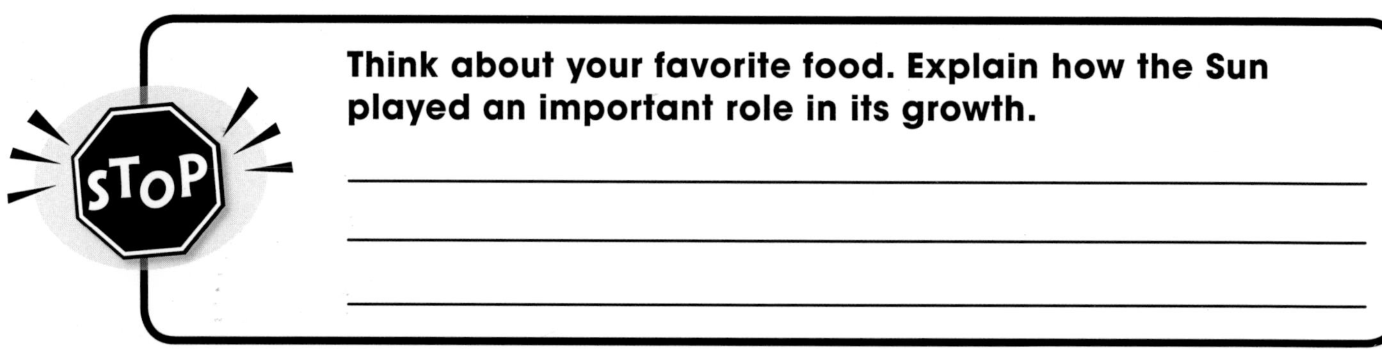

Think about your favorite food. Explain how the Sun played an important role in its growth.

____

____

____

A **producer** is an organism that produces its own food. An example of a producer is a green plant. It takes in energy from the Sun and makes food which is then passed on to **consumers**. A **consumer** is an organism that cannot make its own food. It is called a **consumer** because it depends on others. It gets food by eating other organisms. **Decomposers** play a very important role too. **Decomposers** break down materials in dead organisms. Humans recycle certain things so that we can use them again. **Decomposers** do the same thing. They recycle nutrients from dead organisms and return them to the soil. They can then be used again by **producers**. Imagine that these three kinds of organisms all live in a cycle. They all depend on each other for energy and food. Without each other, they would not survive.

NAME: ______________________________

Producers, Consumers & Decomposers

1. Draw a line between two circles to match up the words with their definitions.

producer

A To reuse something once it has died or has been thrown away

consumer

B The main source of energy for everything living on Earth.

C An organism that breaks down materials in dead organisms.

decomposer

D An organism that depends on others for food.

recycle

E An organism that produces its own food

the sun

Answer the questions in complete sentences.

2. In what way can we divide all organisms? Use words from the reading passage in your answer.

____

____

3. What is the difference between a **producer** and a **consumer**?

____

____

After You Read

NAME: ______________________________

Producers, Consumers & Decomposers

Answer the questions in complete sentences.

4. What is the role of a **decomposer**?

____

____

5. How do producers, consumers, and decomposers all live in a **cycle**?

____

____

Extension & Application

6. Imagine you have just bought your own business. Right now you have too much work so you need to hire some people to work for you. You will need to hire a **PRODUCER**, a **CONSUMER**, and a **DECOMPOSER**. These jobs do not exist in the human world, but for this activity, use your imagination.

You have been given space to advertise these three jobs in the local newspaper. What would you write? Copy down the chart below onto your own piece of paper. You can come up with your own design or you can follow the format below.

You should have **THREE** advertisements to complete this activity, one for each job: **producer**, **consumer**, and **decomposer**.

Newspaper Name - Classifieds

Today's Date: ______________________________

Looking for a: ______________________________

Job Description: ______________________________

____

Salary: ______________________________

Please Apply by: ______________________________

NAME: ______________________________

Food Chains & Food Webs

1. In the square below, draw what you think a chain looks like. Fill the whole square!

a) How does the chain stay together?

____

____

____

____

b) What would happen if you took out one of the chain links?

____

____

____

2. Complete each sentence with a word from the list. Use a dictionary to help you.

organism **web** **chain** **interaction** **nutrients**

a) A [ ] is a complicated structure. Spiders spin them!

b) A relationship between two or more things is called an [ ].

c) [ ] are the healthy things found in food that helps things grow.

d) An [ ] is any individual form of life, for example, a plant or an animal.

e) A [ ] has links in it that are connected. These links hold the chain together.

NAME: ____________________

Food Chains & Food Webs

What Is a Food Chain?

We just learned that all organisms depend on each other for food and energy. We also learned that all food is produced using the Sun's energy. Some organisms use the Sun's energy directly for food (for example, plants). Others eat other organisms because they cannot make their own food. And others break down nutrients in dead organisms to make food for others. We call these producers, consumers, and decomposers. If you look at the drawing to the right, you will see many arrows. These arrows show how each organism is dependent on another organism. It looks like a long chain. We call this the **food chain**. Each part is linked or dependent on another part. It looks like a chain-linked fence in a backyard or a necklace!

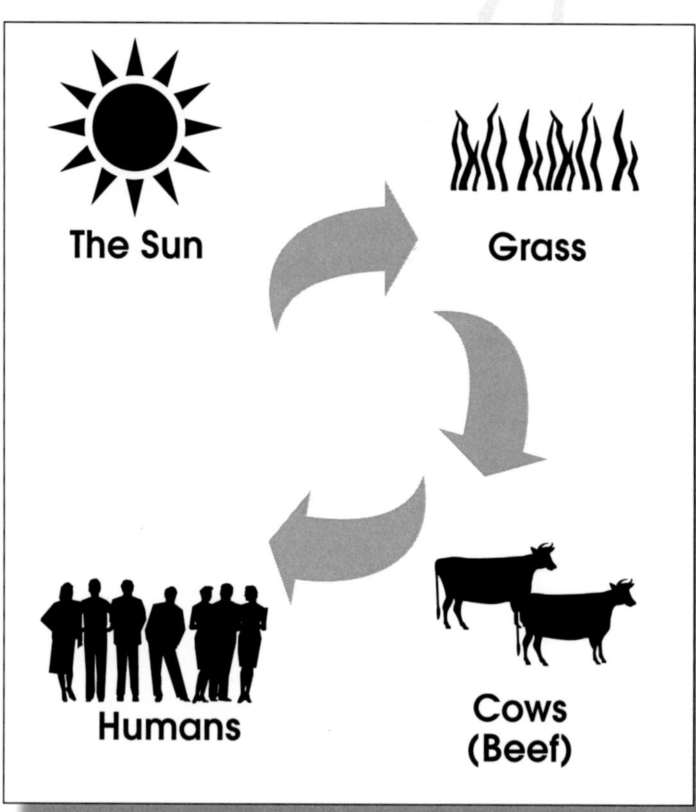

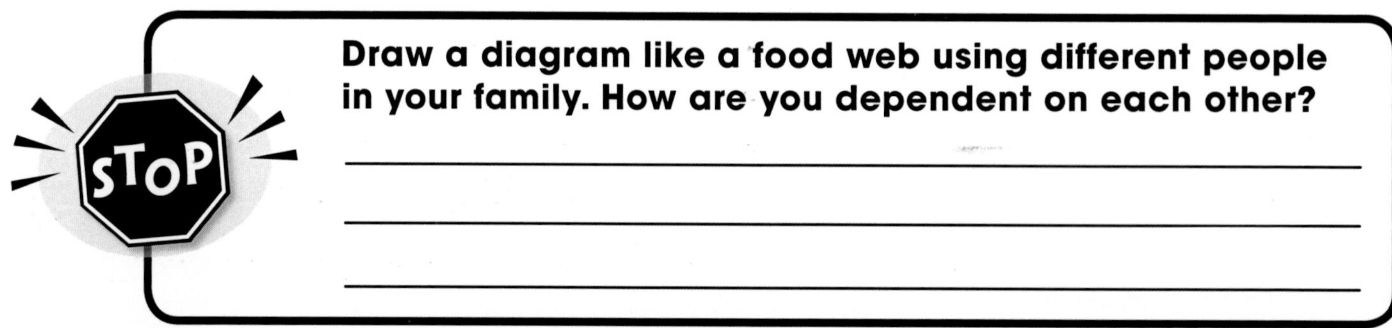

Draw a diagram like a food web using different people in your family. How are you dependent on each other?

____

____

____

Do humans only eat one type of food? Of course not. There are no organisms that eat only one type of food. Every organism depends on more than one other organism for food. That is why the **food chain** looks very busy. In a food chain diagram, every organism would have more than one arrow coming towards it or going away from it. The arrows overlap each other. Have you ever looked closely at a spider's web? The many arrows in a food chain look very similar to a spider's web. That is why we call the busy interactions between organisms a **food web**.

NAME: ______________________________

Food Chains & Food Webs

1. Circle T if the statement is TRUE or F if it is FALSE. If it is false, rewrite the sentence to make it true.

T F **a)** All organisms use the Sun's energy directly for food.

____

T F **b)** Some organisms eat other organisms because they can not make their own food.

____

T F **c)** Arrows in a food web diagram show how organisms depend on other organisms.

____

T F **d)** Not all parts of a food chain are linked.

____

T F **e)** Organisms depend on only one other organism for food.

____

2. Draw a straight line from the word on the left to its definition on the right. Which word is left over? Use the reading passage or a dictionary to help you write out its definition.

1	nutrients	A relationship between two or more things	A
2	food chain	Healthy things found in food that helps things grow	B
3	organism	Any individual form of life	C
4	food web	A diagram showing many food chains. The many arrows show the busy interactions between organisms.	D
5	interaction	______________________________	E

NAME: ______________________

Food Chains & Food Webs

3. **A food chain diagram** shows how organisms depend on each other for food. Look at the food chain diagram below. Explain in your own words how these organisms depend on each other.

The Sun
↓
Grass
↓
Cows (Beef)
↓
Humans

____
____
____
____
____
____
____
____

Extension & Application

4. **SPIN YOUR OWN FOOD WEB!**

Food webs look like spider webs. They show how EACH organism depends on MANY organisms for food. Many arrows criss-cross over each other. This shows how complicated their interactions are.

On the worksheet provided, create your own **food web**. The first box is filled in for you (the Sun). Fill in the rest of the boxes using organisms from the list below. **CHOOSE EIGHT** from the list of twenty organisms. Use research tools to find out what each organism eats. Remember, each organism is dependent on more than one other organism! Use **arrows** to show how these organisms are dependent on each other.

- **Humans**
- **Worm**
- **Rabbit**
- **Grass**
- **Chicken**
- **Cow**
- **Rice**
- **A Deer**
- **Seaweed**
- **Lettuce**
- **Wheat**
- **Beetle**
- **Dog**
- **Mouse**
- **Corn**
- **Ant**
- **Fish**
- **Carrot**
- **Potato**
- **Shark**

NAME: ____________________

Spin Your Own Food Web!

Fill in the boxes using **organisms** from the list (page 28). Find out what each organism eats. Use arrows to show who each organism is dependent on for food. Remember, there should be many arrows. Each organism is dependent on more than one other organism!

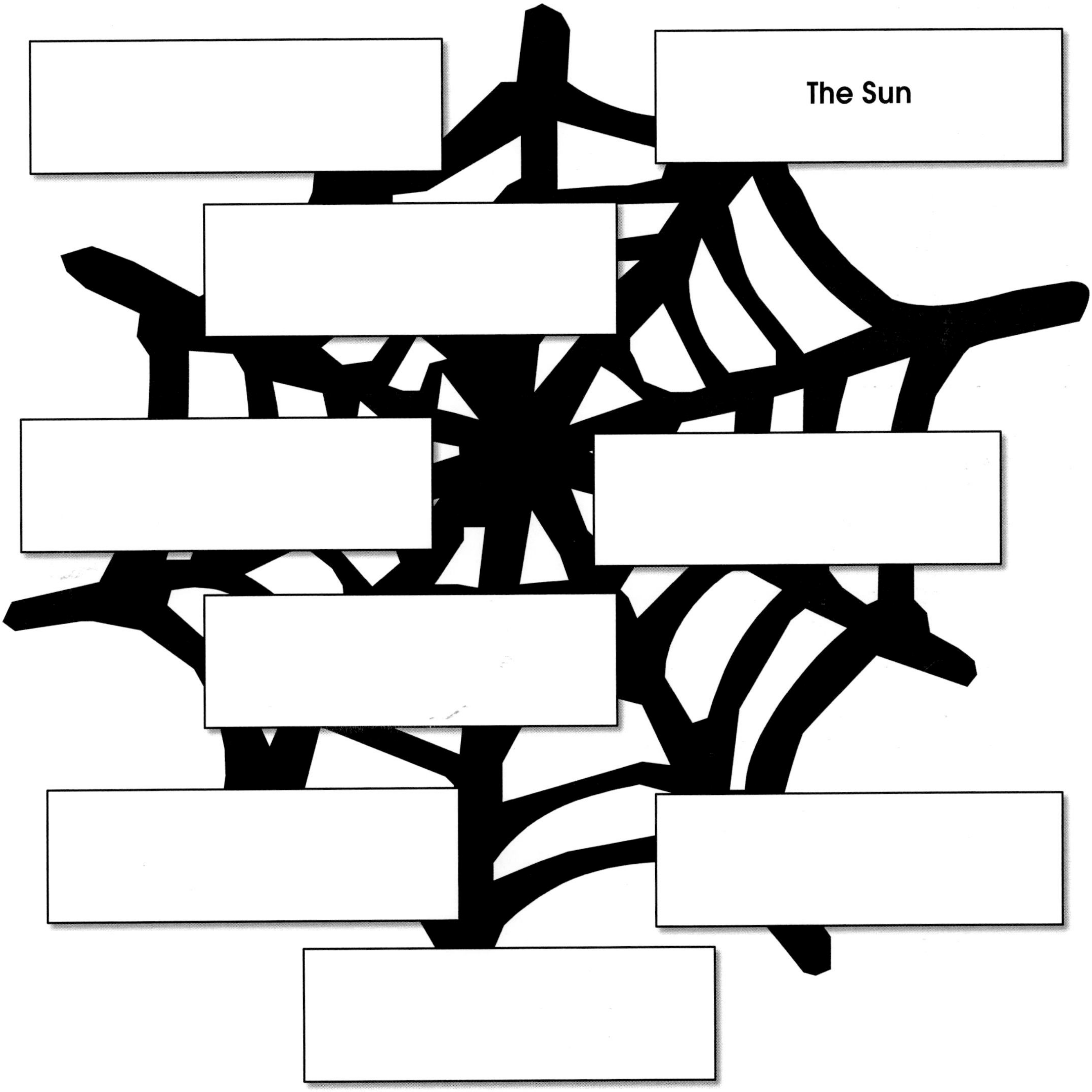

The Sun

Photosynthesis

1. Complete each sentence with a word from the list below. You can use a dictionary for help.

sugar oxygen photosynthesis carbon dioxide leaves energy

a) The word [ ] describes the way that green plants make their own food.

b) We need food to give us [ ] so that we can live a healthy life.

c) Just like humans have arms and legs to collect food, plants have [ ] to help them make their own food.

d) When humans breathe in fresh air, we breathe in oxygen and breathe out [ ].

e) [ ] is very sweet but is not only used by humans to sweeten food. Plants use it too to make food!

f) A gas that is produced by plants during photosynthesis is called [ ].

2. Read the words below. In which group does each thing belong – PLANTS or ANIMALS?

cactus monkey small tree human rose bush snake puppy

PLANTS	ANIMALS

3. Pick TWO things from the above list. Where do you think they get energy from?

a) A ______________ gets energy from ______________________.

b) A ______________ gets energy from ______________________.

NAME: ______________________

Photosynthesis

Did you know that most plants are very lucky? Plants are lucky because they never need to go grocery shopping! They also do not need to spend time cooking! They sit around in soil and wait for sunshine to come. Plants use the Sun to make their food themselves. Humans make food by cooking. We cannot make our own food without buying it or growing it. Plants are the only living things that can make their own food.

Animals breathe in oxygen and breathe out **carbon dioxide**. Green plants do the opposite. They breathe in carbon dioxide and breathe out oxygen. Plants breathe in carbon dioxide through their leaves during the day. From sunlight, green plants mix carbon dioxide and water to make **sugar** and **oxygen**. We all like sugar, don't we? Plants do too. Sugar gives plants energy to grow. We call this whole process **photosynthesis**. It is the process where plants use sunlight, water and carbon dioxide to make food, oxygen and water.

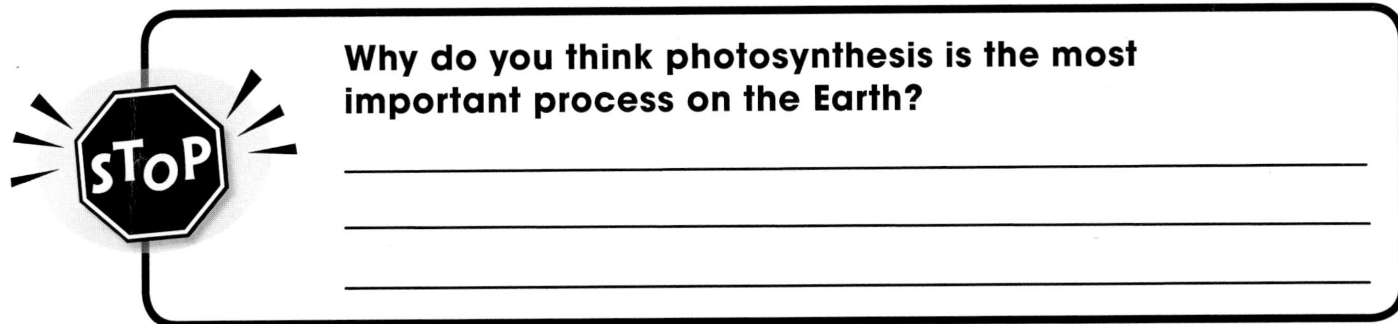

Many animals and plants depend on other plants to survive. That is why **photosynthesis** is so important. If plants could not use the Sun's energy to make food, what would happen? We would not be able to live! Light is so important to plants and plants are so important to us. We can eat so many different things that plants can grow… fruits, nuts, leaves, seeds, and even flowers!

NAME: ______________________

Photosynthesis

1. Put a check mark (✓) next to the answer that is most correct.

a) We can consider plants to be very lucky because they:

- ◯ **A** have leaves to help them grow strong and tall.
- ◯ **B** they are the only living organisms that are able to make their own food.
- ◯ **C** their roots bring them food from the soil.
- ◯ **D** they grow very close to other plants and can help each other find food.

b) How do plants make their own food?

- ◯ **A** They find bugs and other things in the soil close to their roots.
- ◯ **B** They do not need food to grow.
- ◯ **C** They get food from the plants that are living close to them.
- ◯ **D** They use sunlight, water and carbon dioxide to make food.

c) Why is photosynthesis the most important process on our Earth?

- ◯ **A** Many animals and plants depend on plants to survive.
- ◯ **B** Plants do not need energy from sunlight to make food.
- ◯ **C** We would still survive on Earth if plants didn't make food.
- ◯ **D** Only humans depend on plants for energy.

d) Where do plants get most of their energy from?

- ◯ **A** from the people that have planted them in the soil
- ◯ **B** from water, either from a garden hose or rain
- ◯ **C** from the air around them, especially on hot summer days
- ◯ **D** from the sun's energy which is called solar energy

2. Circle T if the statement is TRUE or F if it is FALSE. If it is false, rewrite the sentence to make it true.

T F a) We can eat everything that plants grow, even some flowers.

____

T F b) Humans breathe in carbon dioxide and breathe out oxygen. Plants do the same.

____

T F c) Humans can make their own food just like plants.

____

NAME: ______________________________

Photosynthesis

3. Circle the words that plants use to help them make their own food:

water **vitamins** **oxygen** **carbon dioxide** **Mars bar** **sunlight**

4. Circle the words that are a part of the photosynthesis process:

plants **humans** **sunlight** **fertilizer** **energy** **water**

5. Circle the things that are able to make their own food:

chef **tree** **child** **cactus** **worm** **fern** **plant**

Extension & Application

6. **Imagine You Are The Sun.** You have a huge job on this Earth. Write a **DIARY ENTRY** or a **LETTER** to a friend telling them all about what your day is like as the Sun. Use your imagination as best as you can. Be sure to include specific information you have learned from the reading passage:
   - Who is depending on you for energy?
   - How does that help other things living on Earth?
   - How does your energy help others make food?

   Your diary entry should look similar to the following:

Today's Date (month, day, year): ____________

Dear Diary (or friend's name),

____

____

Sincerely, (your name)

7. **PRETEND YOU ARE A TEACHER!** Using what you have learned from the reading passage, DESIGN A DIAGRAM which would help you explain the process of **photosynthesis** to another student. Remember: assume that the other student knows very little about plants and energy. Be sure to label your diagram!

   You should include the following things in your diagram... Don't forget to use arrows to show relationships between two things!

the sun **water** **oxygen** **carbon dioxide** **sugar** **food**

Before You Read

NAME: ______________________

The Water Cycle

1. Draw a straight line from the word on the left to its definition on the right. You may use a dictionary to help.

1	water cycle	Gathering of objects	A
2	evaporation	The movement of water from land up into the air and then back to the ground	B
3	collection	Water or the amount of water that falls to the Earth	C
4	precipitation	Water turns into vapor or steam	D
5	condensation	Water turns from a vapor into a liquid	E

2. Complete each sentence with a word from the list below. You can use a dictionary for help.

collection **water** **evaporation** **condensation** **precipitation**

a) ______________ is when water falls down to the Earth as rain, snow or hail.

b) When you boil water in a tea kettle, steam is produced. This is called ______________ .

c) ______________ can be a solid, liquid, or a gas.

d) ______________ is when you are gathering something together in one place.

e) When water turns from a vapor into a liquid, it is called ______________ .

NAME: ________________________

The Water Cycle

Pretend there is a full glass of water sitting on your desk right now. Look at the water. Guess how old the water is. Have you ever thought about that? You might have just turned on the tap a minute ago. Does that make the water one minute old? No, it does not. The water might have fallen from the sky a week ago. That still does not make the water one week old. The water itself has been around pretty much as long as the Earth has. It is very old! Think way back to when life on Earth started. The water in your glass was part of the very first ocean. The Earth has an exact amount of water on it. When water goes around and around on our Earth, we call it the **water cycle**.

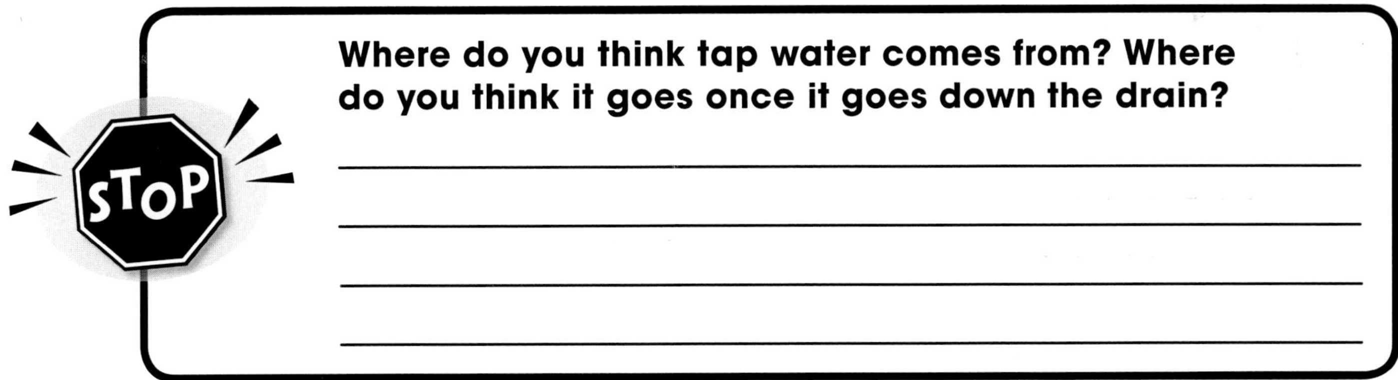

Where do you think tap water comes from? Where do you think it goes once it goes down the drain?

____

____

____

____

The water cycle is made up of four steps: evaporation, condensation, precipitation, and collection. **Evaporation** is the first step. The Sun heats up the water in lakes and oceans. The water turns into vapor or steam. **Condensation** is the next step. Water vapor in the air gets cold and turns back into a liquid. Clouds are formed! **Precipitation** happens when so much water has condensed that air cannot hold it anymore. Clouds let water fall back to Earth. This is rain and snow! **Collection** happens when precipitation falls back to Earth. Water goes into lakes and oceans. It may also fall onto land and soak into the Earth through the soil. Then the cycle starts all over again!

After You Read

NAME: ______________________

The Water Cycle

1. Number the events from 1 to 4 in the order they occur in the WATER CYCLE.

______ **a) Condensation:** Water vapor in the air gets cold and turns back into a liquid. Clouds are formed.

______ **b) Precipitation:** So much water has condensed that air can not hold it anymore.

______ **c) Collection:** Precipitation falls back to Earth through lakes, oceans and through the soil in land.

______ **d) Evaporation:** The Sun heats up from lakes, oceans and land. Water is turned into vapor or steam.

2. Label the diagram below using words from the list.

precipitation **condensation** **evaporation** **collection**

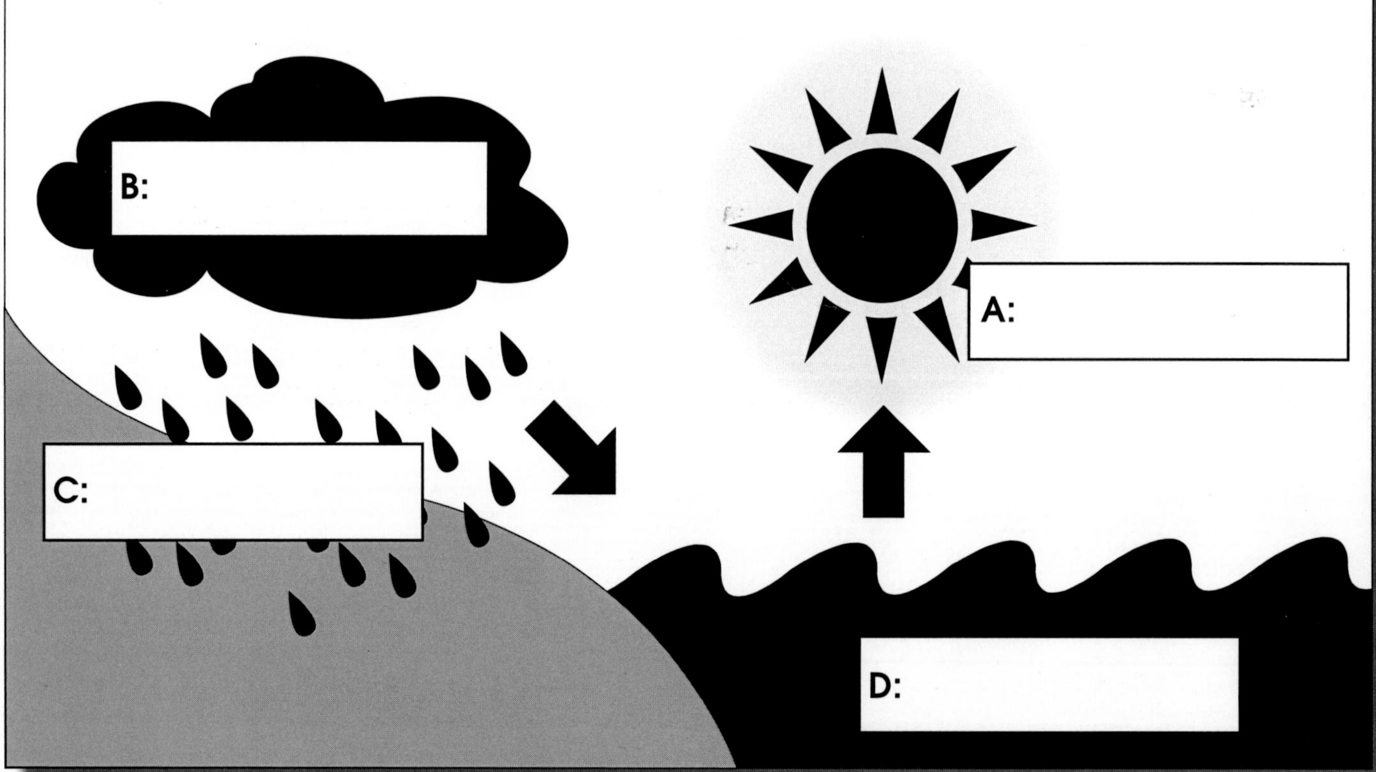

B:

A:

C:

D:

NAME: ______________________________

The Water Cycle

3. **Circle T if the statement is TRUE or F if it is FALSE. If it is false, rewrite the sentence to make it true.**

T F a) Tap water might have fallen from the sky as rain water.

____

T F b) Water from the tap has just been created on Earth.

____

T F c) The amount of water on Earth changes every day.

____

T F d) Evaporation is the last step in the water cycle. It is when water falls back to Earth as rain or snow.

____

T F e) The water cycle shows how water goes around and around on Earth.

____

Extension & Application

4. WRITE A PLAY!

You are the newest play writer in Hollywood. You have a very important job to do. Five hundred people are coming to watch your play called "The Water Cycle" but you haven't written it yet!

You will write a play that will teach the audience how **water cycles around on Earth**. Create a CONVERSATION between the following characters/actors:

- **Water**
- **Evaporation**
- **Condensation**
- **Precipitation**
- **Collection**

Use your conversation to explain what happens to the "water" character at each of these stages in the water cycle. Pretend each stage is a character!

Be creative and use your own sense of humor. A funny play is an enjoyable play!

NAME: ______________________

Microorganisms

1. **A microscope** is used to see something that is too small to see with your own eyes. Pick **THREE** things from the list below. **Draw** what you think they would look like under a microscope. Remember, your drawing will be very close up to the object!

Leaf **Worm** **Fingerprint** **Corn** **Spider** **Grass** **Grain of rice**

_______________ _______________ _______________

2. **Fill in the blanks using a word from the list below. You may use a dictionary to help.**

virus **microscope** **bacteria** **microorganism** **fungi**

a) A ______________ is used to look at something that is too small to see with your own eyes.

b) An organism that needs to be magnified to be seen is called a ______________.

c) ______________ are microorganisms that have only one cell.

d) If someone gets sick with a cold, they have caught a ______________.

e) Organisms that live by taking in nutrients from organic things are called ______________.

NAME: ____________________

Microorganisms

What Is a Microorganism?

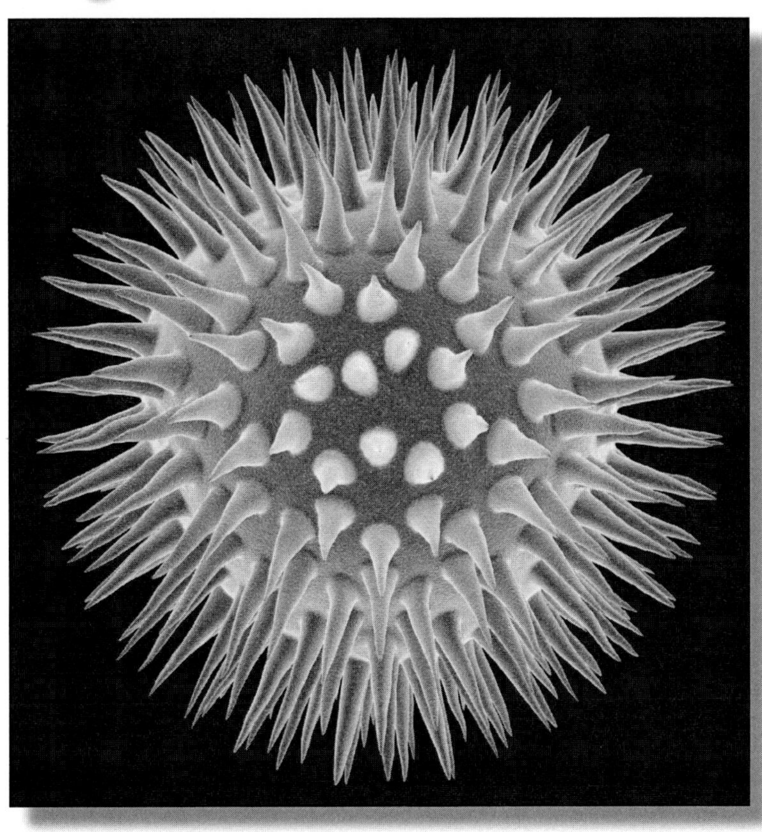

Imagine something that is so small that you can not see it with your own eyes. Have you ever used a **microscope** in Science class to look at something very, very small? Well, you would need to use a microscope if you wanted to look at a microorganism. A **microorganism** is any organism that needs to be magnified to be seen.

Microorganisms are incredibly small but are very important on our Earth. They have a job to do. They are so important that without them, life on Earth would not exist. They recycle dead matter so that it can be reused in the environment.

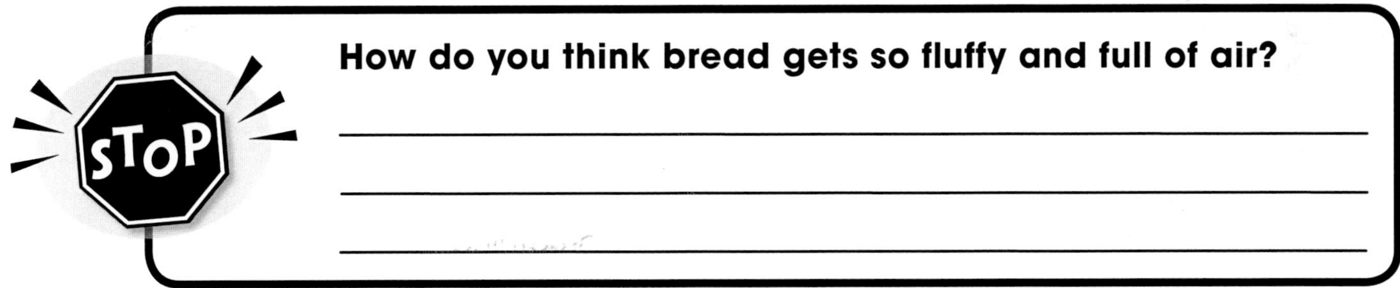

Microorganisms include small organisms such as **bacteria**, **fungi**, and **viruses**. Many microorganisms are useful and some are harmful. Fortunately, most microorganisms are harmless. Humans use microorganisms in our lives every day, but we might not even realize it. For example, fungi are used by doctors to help people feel better. They are also used in making some foods, like cheese and yogurt. Some microorganisms are harmful though. They can cause infections. An infection is caused by a harmful microorganism that is passed from one person to another. Have you ever had a cold because someone else in your class had a cold too? You can see that bacteria can be passed on very easily. It is important to take care of yourself so that you avoid these harmful microorganisms!

After You Read

NAME: ____________________

Microorganisms

1. Put a check mark (✓) next to the answer that is most correct.

a) What could you use to look at something so small you couldn't see it with your eyes?

- ○ **A** Microphone
- ○ **B** Microscope
- ○ **C** Telescope
- ○ **D** A new prescription for your glasses

b) What very important job do microorganisms do on Earth?

- ○ **A** They reproduce with other organisms in their population.
- ○ **B** They organize the lives of organisms in their ecosystem.
- ○ **C** They recycle dead matter so that it can be reused in the environment.
- ○ **D** They don't actually have an important job to do.

c) Microorganisms include which of the following?

- ○ **A** Sunlight, oxygen and carbon dioxide
- ○ **B** Bacteria, food and energy
- ○ **C** Producers, consumers and decomposers
- ○ **D** Bacteria, yeasts, fungi and viruses

d) How do we use microorganisms in a helpful way?

- ○ **A** To help us learn about the environment we live in
- ○ **B** To pass infections from one person to another
- ○ **C** To make some foods and medicine
- ○ **D** To teach us how to recycle things rather than throwing them in the garbage

e) How early can microorganisms be passed on from person to person?

- ○ **A** Microorganisms can never be passed on from person to person.
- ○ **B** Microorganisms can be passed on very easily, just like with the common cold.
- ○ **C** People don't have to avoid harmful microorganisms so bacteria does not matter.
- ○ **D** All microorganisms are harmless so it is good when they get passed on from person to person.

NAME: ______________________________

Microorganisms

2. Divide the word MICROORGANISM into two parts: MICRO and ORGANISM. Use a dictionary to look up the definitions of both words. Then put both parts back together and write your own definition of microorganism.

A **Micro** (dictionary): ______________________________

B **Organism** (dictionary): ______________________________

C Own definition of **microorganism**:

____

Extension & Application

3. Be a Virus Detective!

Send out a warning statement. Choose ONE virus from the list below. Use an encyclopedia, a dictionary and the internet to research the virus. Use the format below to begin your "Warning" statement. In your warning, you should include:

- The virus name
- How the virus is harmful
- How it is passed from one person to another

Influenza **measles** **Norwalk** **herpes** **HIV**

WARNING: Virus Found
Virus name:
Information:

4. The Secret Ingredient to Bread!

For this activity, pretend you are a baker. You will **RESEARCH A RECIPE** to make bread. Use the chart below to fill in a recipe card. Make sure you use step-by-step instructions. Don't forget to include yeast. It's the secret ingredient!

Recipe ______________________________

Ingedients:

Step 1: ______________________________

Step 2: ______________________________

Step 3: ______________________________

The Rabbit Bean Population!

YOU WILL NEED:

- Two colors of dried beans
- Graph paper
- Pencil or marker

Begin with two beans. You should have two different colored beans. One bean is a **male** rabbit and the other color bean is a **female** rabbit.

You are now going to **record the rabbit population for the next five years**. You won't be spending five real years on this project, don't worry!

Each year, each pair of rabbits gives birth to two rabbits – one male and one female. **SET UP A GRAPH** to record how the rabbit population will grow. Each year you will add beans to your population pile. These beans will be the new rabbits that are born each year. Record the numbers on your graph paper.

How many rabbits are in the population after five years? **Remember: after the first year, there are many pairs that will give birth to two new rabbits. The population will grow quickly!**

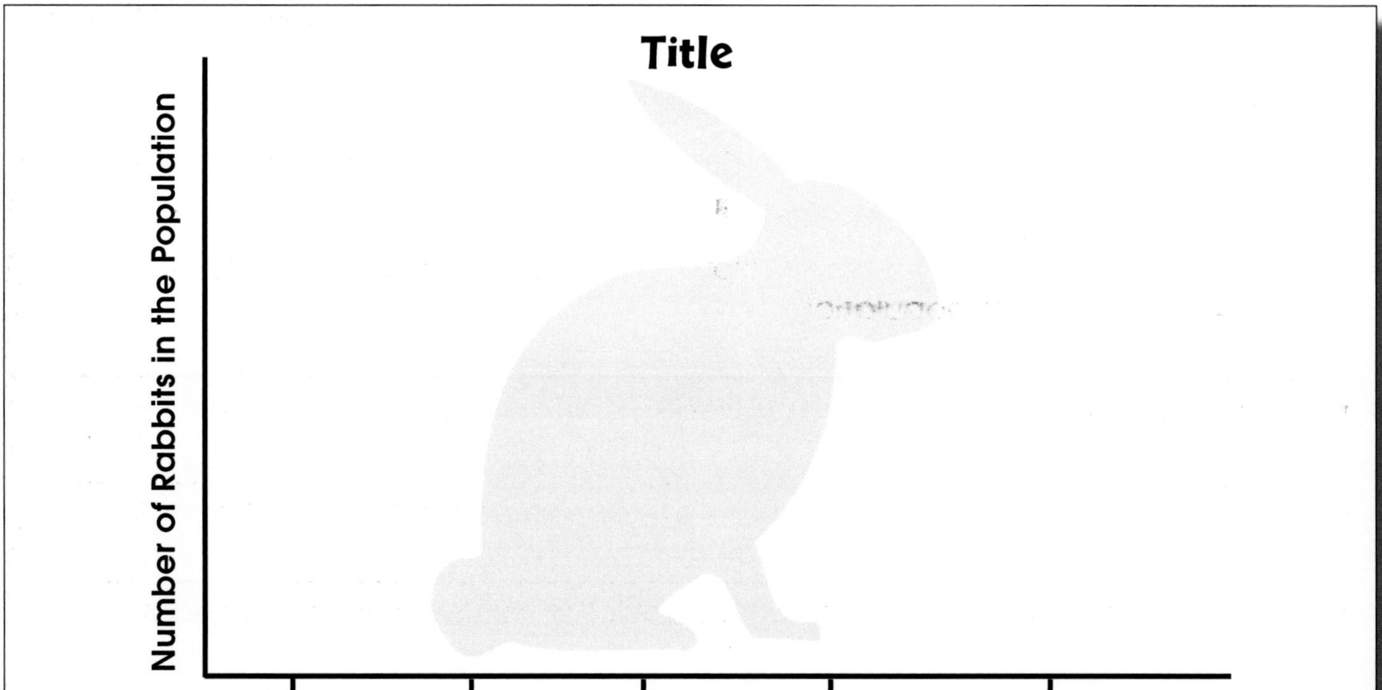

Title

Number of Rabbits in the Population

1 2 3 **Years** 4 5

A Scientist Investigates an Ecosystem!

FOR THIS ACTIVITY, you will need to gather or find the following things:

An outdoor area (for example, the school field or a patch of a garden)

- **A long piece of string**
- **Magnifying glass**
- **Thermometer**
- **Popsicle sticks**
- **Paper and pencil**
- **Small gardening tools**

WHAT YOU WILL DO:

1. Pick a small patch of land to investigate.
2. Use the string to mark off the area you have chosen.
3. On your piece of paper, record everything you can see about your ecosystem. Include all biotic (living) and abiotic (non-living) things. How are these organisms working and living together?
4. Using the thermometer, record temperatures in your ecosystem.
5. Turn over a small patch of grass or flip over a rock. Record what you see beneath the surface.

Now it's time to record your conclusions!

IN YOUR RECORDS, answer the following questions:

- Consider the variety of biotic and abiotic things you found in your ecosystem. Which was the largest population?

____

- How do each of these organisms survive in your ecosystem?

____

- Can you think of any other populations that could survive in your ecosystem?

____

- Can you think of any populations which would <u>not</u> survive in your ecosystem? Why not?

____

Build Your Own Ecosystem!

We have talked and read about so many ecosystems. Now it is time to build your own!

COLLECT THE FOLLOWING MATERIALS:

- **Gravel or small rocks**
- **Soil/dirt**
- **A jar or bottle** (with a large enough top to put your hand into)
- **A lid for your jar or bottle to seal it** (you can seal it with tape if you think air can get into the jar)
- **A few plants from the school yard or a garden**
- **Small animals from the garden** (worms, snails, slugs, etc.)
- **Wood, garden rocks or branches to make it look like a real ecosystem**

WHAT YOU WILL DO:

1. Put a large handful of gravel or small rocks in the bottom of your jar.
2. Add a large handful of soil.
3. Plant the plants into the soil. Try to choose plants that fit into your jar. If it's a small jar, only use small plants. If you put too many plants in, they will not survive!
4. If you think your ecosystem needs water, add a bit of water. Don't over water your ecosystem though!
5. **This is the fun bit...** choose some animals. Use anything you can find in the school yard or garden. Remember, choose small animals. You want these animals to survive!
6. Close your ecosystem. Put the lid on or use tape to seal it.

Now it's time to record your observations!

ON A PIECE OF PAPER, record the following things:

- Size of your container (you may want to draw a picture of your ecosystem)
- Number and type of plants and animals you used
- How much soil you used
- What is happening in your system? Count your animals and record if your plants are growing. Have all of your plants and animals survived?

Have fun building your own ecosystem!

Make Smaller Ecological Footprints!

An ecological "footprint" is the food, water and space that a living thing needs to grow and survive in an ecosystem.

Every thing that lives on Earth has a "footprint". Big things have larger footprints than little things. For example, a big tree needs more things to survive than a small flower!

Humans have ecological footprints too. Sometimes humans have very big ecological footprints. We use more things than we actually need. If we could make our ecological footprints smaller, then there would be more in our world to share with each other.

How can we make smaller footprints? Your job to find out how!

You are now are the teacher. Once you have completed this activity, you will visit another classroom in your school. You will present your bulletin board. Your board will teach others how humans can make smaller footprints. It will teach others how we can stop overusing our own environment.

USE THE FOLLOWING MATERIALS to put together a bulletin board:

- **Bristol board**
- **Magazine pictures**
- **Scissors, glue, markers**
- **Any other materials you can think of!**

Here are a few ideas to get you started.

To make smaller footprints, humans could ...

- Recycle paper and containers
- Ride a bike rather than driving a car
- Take a shower instead of a bath to save water
- Pick up litter
- Turn the lights off to save energy
- Any more ideas??

NAME: ______________________

Crossword Puzzle!

Across

1. group of things that live and work together in an environment

4. something that is not living

5. a microorganism that only has one cell

7. to use something again

8. used to look at something that is too small to see with eyes

10. when water turns from a vapor into a liquid

13. an organism that needs to be magnified to be seen

Down

1. food gives us this so that we can live a healthy life

2. tastes sweet and plants use it to make food

3. when water turns into vapor or steam

5. something that is living

6. an organism that depends on others for food

8. the path of water going around and around on Earth

9. when you gather something in one place

11. group of similar individuals living in the same area

12. organism that breaks down materials in dead organisms

14. something contagious that makes you feel unwell

15. a diagram that shows many food chains

NAME: ______________________________

Word Search

Find all of the words in the Word Search. Words are written horizontally, vertically, or diagonally, and some are even be backwards.

abiotic	decomposer	leaf	producer
bacteria	ecosystem	microorganism	recycle
balance	energy	nutrients	reproduce
biotic	environment	organism	succession
composition	evaporation	oxygen	sun
condensation	foodchain	photosynthesis	virus
consumer	fungi	population	web

b	a	c	t	e	r	i	a	v	e	e	c	n	a	l	a	b	n
w	o	d	r	e	c	y	c	l	e	r	t	h	t	n	v	b	u
e	e	r	c	o	n	d	e	n	s	a	t	i	o	n	z	c	s
n	t	z	g	w	e	f	g	t	y	x	b	q	e	r	z	o	t
v	n	c	w	a	r	n	u	t	r	i	e	n	t	s	q	n	s
i	o	v	s	q	n	w	e	c	o	s	y	s	t	e	m	s	h
r	i	b	d	w	e	i	j	w	w	r	w	j	h	s	a	u	e
o	t	b	f	y	n	f	s	r	e	d	b	k	g	d	p	m	e
n	a	n	g	u	b	g	h	m	d	c	v	f	f	e	h	e	h
m	r	y	g	r	e	n	e	t	w	w	a	b	d	c	o	r	e
e	o	g	h	g	v	h	r	y	k	e	r	g	s	o	t	n	e
n	p	h	r	n	o	i	t	a	l	u	p	o	p	m	o	l	y
t	a	p	j	e	c	y	b	y	n	g	d	x	w	p	s	r	k
v	v	j	r	h	p	j	v	c	g	d	h	y	e	o	y	y	s
r	e	k	k	o	q	r	c	u	i	n	m	g	r	s	n	e	u
e	t	y	v	j	d	u	o	o	w	t	b	e	t	e	t	d	c
b	b	i	i	k	t	u	x	d	d	s	o	n	y	r	h	s	c
n	i	g	r	b	r	k	c	e	u	w	h	i	h	m	e	c	e
m	o	n	u	e	e	r	w	e	d	c	a	v	b	n	s	n	s
r	t	u	s	w	q	w	e	r	r	y	e	d	f	a	i	v	s
y	i	f	o	o	d	c	h	a	i	n	h	g	j	k	s	v	i
k	c	c	c	o	m	p	o	s	i	t	i	o	n	r	y	e	o
g	q	e	m	s	i	n	a	g	r	o	o	r	c	i	m	s	n

After You Read

NAME: ______________________________

Comprehension Quiz

Part A

Circle T if the statement is TRUE or F if it is FALSE.

8

T F **1.** A rainforest, a puddle, our Earth, and a handful of soil are all examples of ecosystems.

T F **2.** As long as organisms look similar, they are part of the same population.

T F **3.** Succession describes what happens when something changes over a long period of time.

T F **4.** Producers, consumers, and decomposers depend on each other for energy and food.

T F **5.** Food chain shows how organisms rely on themselves to find food and energy.

T F **6.** Photosynthesis is the process where plants use sunlight, water, and carbon dioxide to make food, oxygen, and water.

T F **7.** The water cycle shows how water goes up through the roots of a tree, and falls back to the ground through evaporation.

T F **8.** Microorganisms include big organisms like bacteria. They are so big that you need a telescope to see them.

Part B

Label the diagram by doing the following:

6

1. Write the stages below on the diagram to show each stage in the **water cycle**.

- evaporation
- condensation
- precipitation
- collection

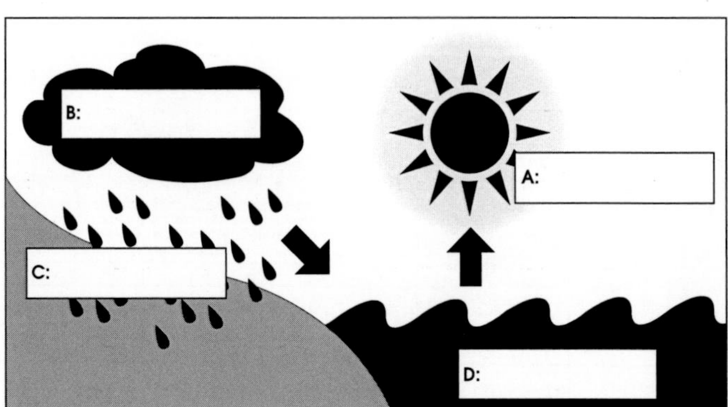

2. Use a colored pencil to show the **path of the water** running through the water cycle.

3. What **shape** does your path make?

____

SUBTOTAL: /14

NAME: ______________________

After You Read

Comprehension Quiz

Part C

1. Describe what an **ecosystem** is. Give two examples of ecosystems and list what you might find living in each ecosystem. 4

____

____

____

2. What two things are important to remember when describing a **population**? Give an example to show you understand the meaning of a population. 3

____

____

____

3. Do **ecosystems change** over time? Describe **how** an ecosystem might change. 3

____

____

4. What is the difference between a **producer**, a **consumer** and a **decomposer**? 3

____

____

____

5. Explain how **microorganisms** might be **helpful** <u>and</u> **harmful** to humans 3

____

____

____

SUBTOTAL: /16

NAME: ______________________

What Do We Classify?

1. Fill in each blank with a word from the list. You may use a dictionary to help.

classify **organism** **senses** **biologist** **category**

a) A group of things that are classified together is called a [ ].

b) To [ ] something means to divide things into groups based on similarities.

c) People use their five [ ] (sight, touch, smell, sound, taste) to describe something.

d) Someone that studies living things is called a [ ].

e) A living thing such as a plant or animal is called a(n) [ ].

2. Look at the word BIOLOGIST. Can you find the root of this word? Use a dictionary to find the definition of BIOLOGY and write it in the box below. Underneath your definition, draw a picture showing a biologist hard at work.

NAME: ______________________________

What Do We Classify?

Think about an elephant. In your mind, can you picture what it looks like? How would you describe it to someone who has never seen one before? You probably visualized a large trunk, gray leathery skin, big ears, heavy feet and a skinny tail. Is that what you imagined?

Everything we just described used your eyes to describe the elephant. You just **classified** an elephant! To **classify** something means to group or to categorize something based on something about them. This time, you used your own eyes to put the elephant into a group of animals that, for example, have gray skin.

Elephants and other **organisms** do not only have to be classified by what they look like. You could classify organisms using another **sense**. You could use your sense of touch, smell, sound, or even taste! Not that you ever want to know what an elephant tastes like!

STOP

Can you describe an elephant using your senses of smell and touch?

____

____

____

Biologists are people that study living things. Part of their job is to classify organisms. They need to organize all things that live on the Earth! They classify organisms into different **categories** or groups. Biologists know that if two organisms look very similar, then they are likely related. Do people ever tell you that you look like your brother or sister? You probably look similar because you are related. You are part of the same family!

After You Read

NAME: ____________________

What Do We Classify?

1. Put a check mark (✓) next to the answer that best finishes the sentence.

a) You can describe an elephant using the following senses:

- ○ **A** just sight (your own eyes).
- ○ **B** all senses (sight, sound, taste, touch, smell).
- ○ **C** it's hard to describe an elephant because it is so big.
- ○ **D** a dictionary and a camera.

b) To classify something means to...

- ○ **A** say whether they are good or bad.
- ○ **B** divide something based on their age.
- ○ **C** group or categorize something based on one of their characteristics.
- ○ **D** study how it survives in its environment.

c) Biologists are people that study...

- ○ **A** the biosphere.
- ○ **B** only humans and how they interact with each other.
- ○ **C** rocks and minerals.
- ○ **D** living things.

d) Biologists know that if two organisms look very similar, then they...

- ○ **A** are likely related.
- ○ **B** must live in the same environment.
- ○ **C** must eat the exact same food for energy.
- ○ **D** are part of the same population.

2. Circle the word True if the statement is true. Circle the word False if it is false.

a) We can classify a mouse by saying that it is an animal with gray skin.

True **False**

b) Organisms have to be classified by what they look like.

True **False**

c) Biologists study both living and non-living things.

True **False**

d) When biologists classify, they look for similarities and difference between organisms.

True **False**

What Do We Classify?

Answer the questions in complete sentences.

3. What senses could you use to describe an animal? Give an example for each.

____

____

4. What is the most important job that a biologist has?

____

5. How do biologists classify organisms?

____

Extension and Application

6. Use your senses to describe an animal of your choice!

Your job is to classify an animal. It can be any animal you like! **Pick one animal** and use the five senses to describe your animal.

On your piece of paper, create a chart that shows the following 5 senses and your descriptions:

- sight
- touch
- smell
- taste
- sound

7. You are the World's #1 Biologist!

You have been hired as the country's leading biologist to work on a project. Congratulations! Your job is to classify the following 10 animals. The tricky part is that you have not been told **how** to classify these animals. It is up to you! You will copy the 10 animals down onto your paper and then put on your biologist uniform and start your work! Remember, a biologist uses their senses to classify organisms. You will need to put these animals into groups. Clue: Look for similarities and differences between these animals... You may use research tools for help.

Monkey	**Dog**	**Bear**
Kangaroo	**Tiger**	**Frog**
Giraffe	**Fox**	**Whale**
Fish		

Before You Read

NAME: ______________________________

Formal Classification

1. Draw a line from the word on the left to its matching definition. Which word is left over? Use the reading passage or a dictionary to help you write out its definition.

1	biologist	when you group or categorize something based on a characteristic	A
2	classification	the classification group that divides each kingdom	B
3	kingdom	a person who studies living things	C
4	phylum	the largest classification group that represents all animals or plants	D
5	class	the classification group that divides each phylum	E
6	family	the classification group that divides each class	F
7	species	______________________________ ______________________________	G

2. In the space below, draw how you would classify the following foods: orange, carrot, broccoli, apple, lemon, lettuce, potato, zucchini. Use pictures to show your classification!

NAME: ______________________________

Formal Classification

Do you remember what the word **classification** means? Remember, it can be applied to many things. In science though, it describes how **biologists** group and categorize living organisms. We looked at an elephant and classified it by what it looks like. Biologists do this too but they classify living things in more detail.

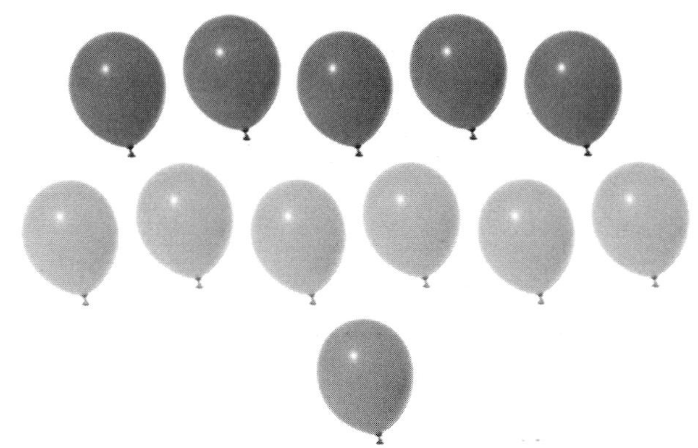

How are phone numbers in a phone book classified? When you are looking for someone's phone number, do you have to look through everybody's name to find the number?

____

____

When you go into a music store to buy the #1 single on the music charts, do you have to look through every CD in the store to find it? That would take hours! What do you do first? You find the category. Is it a pop, rock, rap or punk song? Then you look for the name of the artist, and then the name of the song. Scientists have to do the same thing if they are looking for one specific animal. It would take hours to look through all the animals that live on Earth. There are thousands of different kinds of animals! Scientists **classify** animals. They look for differences and similarities to divide them into smaller groups. Do you agree that this would make it easier to find and study animals?

Let's look at the categories that scientists use to classify animals. Is it enough to just group something in the "animal" category? No, scientists divide animals into the following categories:

Kingdom: the animal kingdom is split into several phylum groups
Phylum: each phylum is split into smaller groups called classes
Class: each class is split into families
Family: each family is split into more than one genus
Genus: each genus is split into species
Species: finally at the bottom, a species is a single organism!

After You Read

NAME: ______________________________

Formal Classification

1. Circle the word True if the statement's true. Circle the word False if it's false.

a) Classification describes how biologists group and categorize living organisms.

True **False**

b) Classifying animals makes it harder for biologists to find an animal they are looking for.

True **False**

c) When biologists classify, they only look for similarities between animals.

True **False**

d) A species is at the bottom of the classification groups. It is a single organism!

True **False**

e) There are 2 categories that biologists divide animals into: animals with four legs, and animals with two legs.

True **False**

2. Circle the answer that best completes each sentence.

a) The animal ______________ is split into several phylum groups.

population **kingdom**

b) Classification describes how biologists group and ______________ living organisms.

categorize **study**

c) When biologists classify animals, they look for ______________ and similarities to divide them into smaller groups.

categories **differences**

NAME: ______________________________

Formal Classification

Answer each question with a complete sentence.

3. How is classifying music in a store similar to classifying animals?

____

4. How do biologists make it easier to find and study animals?

____

5. What categories do biologists use to classify animals? Use the proper terms found in the reading passage.

____

Extension and Application

6. Your new grocery store needs to be reorganized!

You are the proud new owner of a fine food grocery store! Your store is very successful but there is one problem: the previous owner did not organize the food into any categories! It's a mess! Food is piled on top of other food. There is no order! People cannot find what they are looking for.

It is your job as the new owner to reorganize and **classify** your food so that it is easier for customers to find what they are looking for. Imagine what kinds of food you would sell in your store. Come up with at least 10 different items.

On a piece of paper, either draw a picture or write a story about how you would reorganize your store. Customers will appreciate your work!

7. An animal gets classified!

You are a research biologist and you have a job to do: to formally classify an animal. Choose one animal and research its formal classification. You will need to use various research tools for this activity (internet or encyclopedia). Once you have chosen your animal, write down information you find on the following classification categories:

- kingdom
- phylum
- class
- family
- genus
- species

Before You Read

NAME: ______________________

Warm-blooded vs. Cold-blooded Animals

1. In the squares below, draw pictures of animals that you think are WARM-BLOODED. Write your answers on the line in the square.

2. In the squares below, draw pictures of animals that you think are COLD-BLOODED. Write your answers on the line in the square.

3. Complete each sentence with a word from the list. Use a dictionary to help you.

cold-blooded **warm-blooded** **solar energy** **environment**

a) When a ______________________ animal is in a cold climate, its body temperature is cold.

b) The energy that the sun gives off is called ______________________.

c) The surroundings where an animal lives is called its ______________________.

d) ______________________ animals are able to stay at the same body temperature no matter where they live.

NAME: ____________________

Warm-blooded vs. Cold-blooded Animals

What is the difference between cold-blooded animals and warm-blooded animals? The most obvious guess is that cold-blooded animals have cold blood and warm-blooded animals have warm blood. The answer is actually a little bit different.

Cold-blooded animals cannot control their own body temperature. Instead, their body temperature changes, depending on the temperature of their **environment**. **Warm-blooded** animals are able to stay at the same body temperature no matter where they live. Let's look at each of these kinds of animals in more detail.

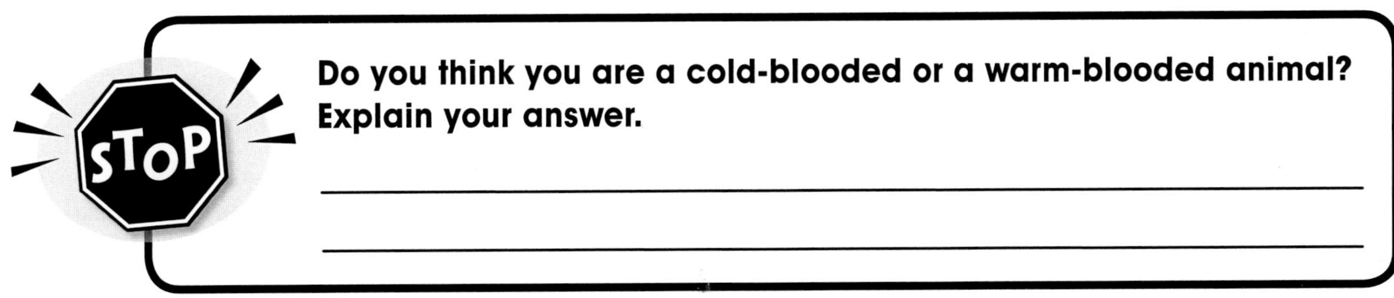

Do you think you are a cold-blooded or a warm-blooded animal? Explain your answer.

____

____

Reptiles, amphibians, and fish are all examples of **cold-blooded animals**. They use **solar energy** (energy from the sun) to control their body temperature. So if the weather is hot, the animal is hot. If the weather is cold, the animal is cold. Have you ever seen a frog sun itself on a rock? It is not trying to get a suntan! The frog suns itself to absorb heat from the sun. What does a frog do when it is too warm out? It finds cool shelter to cool down its body temperature. Smart animal!

Humans, mammals, and birds are all examples of **warm-blooded animals**. Their body temperature stays the same no matter what. Even if the temperature of their environment changes, their body temperature stays the same. They are able to control how much heat their bodies produce. They are also able to control how much heat their bodies lose. They are also smart animals!

After You Read

NAME: ______________________________

Warm-blooded vs. Cold-blooded Animals

1. Circle the answer that best completes each sentence.

a) Cold-blooded animals cannot control their own ______________________.

energy **body temperature**

b) A cold-blooded animal's body temperature depends on the temperature of their ______________.

environment **blood**

c) Cold-blooded animals use ______________________ to control their body temperature.

oxygen **solar energy**

d) Humans and birds are examples of ______________-blooded animals.

cold **warm**

e) Warm-blooded animals are able to control how much ______________ they produce and lose.

heat **energy**

2. Circle the word True if the statement's true. Circle the word False if it's false.

a) A fish is a good example of a warm-blooded animal.

True **False**

b) The difference between cold-blooded and warm-blooded animals is the temperature of their blood.

True **False**

c) A frog might cool its body temperature down by burying itself under a rock.

True **False**

d) Warm-blooded animals are able to control how much heat their bodies produce.

True **False**

e) No matter what temperature the water is, a fish's body temperature always stays the same.

True **False**

NAME: ______________________

Warm-blooded vs. Cold-blooded Animals

3. Classify the following animals into two groups: WARM-BLOODED ANIMALS and COLD-BLOODED ANIMALS. You might need to use research tools to find out more about each animal. Once you have divided them, explain what the difference is between the two groups.

frog human snail eagle dog spider

a) Cold-blooded Animals **Warm-blooded Animals**

______________________ ______________________

______________________ ______________________

______________________ ______________________

b) The difference between cold-blooded and warm-blooded animals is

____

Extension and Application

4. Design a Poster! We read about how the cold-blooded frog controls its body temperature. It might lie on a sunny rock to warm up its body. Or, it might bury under a rock to cool off its body. Use your imagination to think of what the following cold-blooded animals might do to control their body temperature. **Pick one** of the animals from the list below. Draw a picture showing these two things:

- how the animal warms up its body temperature
- how the animal cools off its body temperature

snake lizard crocodile eel salamander

Don't forget to label your picture. Use your imagination!

5. A conversation between a cold-blooded animal and a warm-blooded animal! Pretend you hear a conversation between a **cold-blooded animal** and a **warm-blooded animal**. Using a dialogue structure (Animal #1 says..., Animal #2 says....) write down the conversation you hear. Your conversation should include the following information:

- the names of the animals (pick two)
- what makes them either cold-blooded or warm-blooded
- how they control their body temperature
- the difference between the two animals

Before You Read

NAME: ______________________

Vertebrates

1. Draw a line from the word on the left to its matching definition. Which word is left over? Use the reading passage or a dictionary to help you write out its definition.

1	vertebrae	an animal that has a backbone	A
2	vertebrate	an animal that does **not** have a backbone	B
3	invertebrate	the stringy bands of tissue that connect the nervous system with other organs	C
4	nerve	the bones that form a backbone	D
5	tissue	______________________ ______________________	E

2. Look at the matched definitions in the question above. Use each vocabulary word in your own sentence. Make sure your sentence shows that you understand what the word means.

a) vertebrate ______________________

____

b) invertebrate ______________________

____

c) nerve ______________________

____

d) tissue ______________________

____

Vertebrates

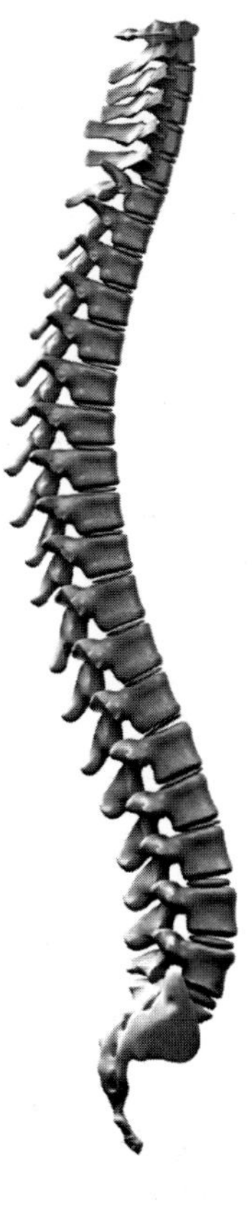

All animals can be classified into two groups: **vertebrates** and **invertebrates**. How do we tell them apart? Here is a clue: What do humans have inside them that make them stand up straight and tall? Yes, a backbone! Humans are classified into a category in the animal kingdom called vertebrates. **Vertebrates** are animals that have a backbone (a "**vertebrae**"). **Invertebrates** do not have a backbone.

STOP

Can you think of THREE examples of vertebrates besides humans?

____

____

____

____

____

Vertebrates are the most advanced organisms on Earth. What makes them so special are their backbones. Think of the human body. We all have **nerves** that run along our back. **Nerves** are the stringy bands of **tissue** that connect the nervous system with other organs. These nerves can't stand up on their own! They need support and protection. That's why vertebrates have backbones.

There are 50 000 vertebrates on Earth. That seems like a lot, but compared to invertebrates, there are not that many species of vertebrates. Vertebrates are very, very intelligent. This includes you! Most vertebrates have very advanced nervous systems. I bet you don't think a goldfish is very smart. A goldfish is a vertebrate though. Compared to a tiny invertebrate, a goldfish is as smart as Einstein!

After You Read

NAME: ______________________

Vertebrates

1. Circle the word True if the statement is true. Circle the word False if it is false.

   a) The main difference between vertebrates and invertebrates is that one has a backbone and the other does not.

      True **False**

   b) Vertebrates are the least advanced organisms on Earth.

      True **False**

   c) Nerves cannot stand up on their own. That's why vertebrates have backbones!

      True **False**

   d) There are only ten different kinds of vertebrates.

      True **False**

   e) Vertebrates are very, very smart. Even goldfish are smart!

      True **False**

2. Write each word besides its meaning. There is ONE word that does NOT have a matching definition! Use the reading passage to write a definition for the remaining word.

   vertebrate **invertebrate** **nerve** **tissue**

   [ ] a) An animal that does not have a backbone.

   [ ] b) A group of cells that have a special job to do, or a specific function.

   [ ] c) An animal that has a backbone.

   [ ] d) ____.

Vertebrates

3. **a)** Circle the animals that can be classified as **vertebrates**:

snail **human** **grizzly bear** **snake** **deer**

b) Circle the words that are associated with a **vertebrate**:

backbone **nerves** **insect** **tissue** **spiders**

c) Circle the words that describe the functions of a **backbone**:

support **intelligence** **protection** **food** **oxygen**

Extension and Application

4. **A Backbone Illustration!** Pretend you have just graduated from drawing school and you have been given your first job. You have been hired to illustrate a book on human anatomy. **Anatomy** studies the physical features of an animal, in this case, a human! You will use research tools (the internet and books) to gather information about what a backbone looks like. Can you picture what your own backbone might look like?

On a blank piece of paper, **draw a picture of the human backbone**. Remember that it is very important that anatomy drawings are **labeled** properly. There might be many details that you want to include in your drawing, so use a pencil.

5. **One of 50 000 Vertebrates!**

There are 50 000 vertebrates living on Earth! This means you have A LOT of choice. **Pick one** vertebrate. (Use your imagination – pick an animal you have not read about yet. Or even better, one you have never heard of before!).

Design a brochure with information in it about your vertebrate. In your brochure, include:

- the name of your vertebrate
- a drawing of your vertebrate (use a pencil!)
- the vertebrate's formal classification (kingdom, phylum, class, order, etc.)
- why your animal can be classified as a vertebrate
- any other interesting information about your animal

Use the graphic organizer on the next page to help you collect your information. Make your brochure as visually appealing as possible! Use colored pencils or markers to add color.

NAME: ______________________

One of 50,000 Vertebrates!

Name of Vertebrate

Why is the animal a vertebrate?

Illustration

Formal Classification

Kingdom:
Phylum:
Class:
Family:
Genus:
Species:

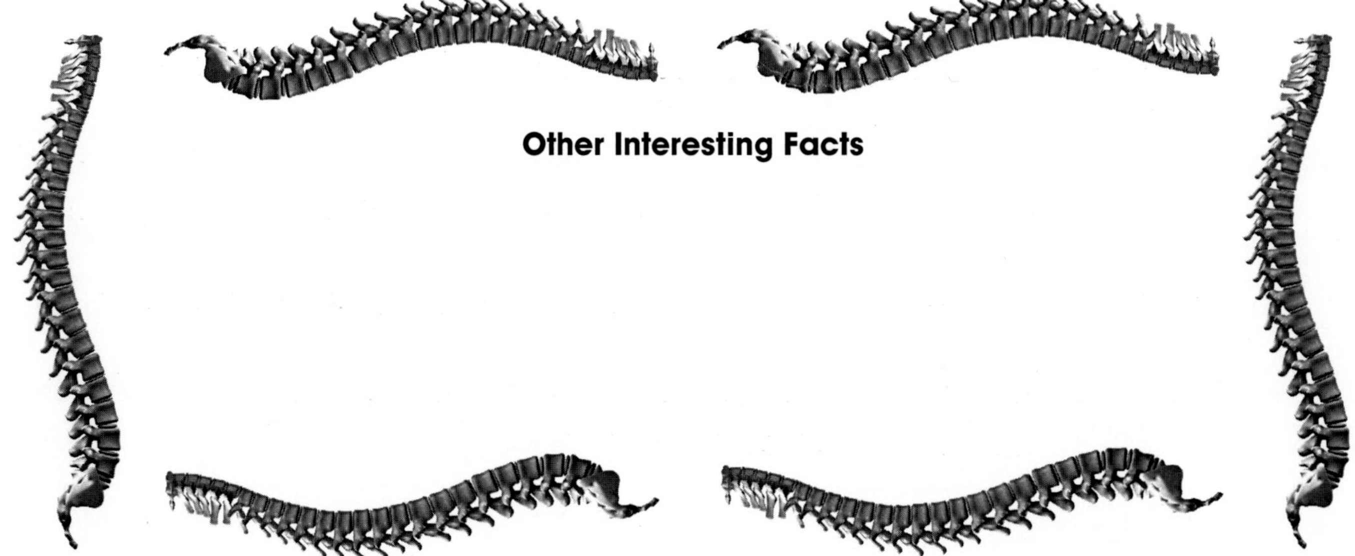

Other Interesting Facts

NAME: ______________________

Invertebrates

1. Match the word on the left to its definition on the right. You may use a dictionary to help.

1	invertebrate	the group of invertebrates that includes spiders.	A
2	insect	describes something where the left side is the mirror image of the right side.	B
3	mollusk	the group of invertebrates that includes snails and slugs.	C
4	arachnid	an animal that does not have a backbone	D
5	symmetrical	the group of invertebrates that includes butterflies, flies, and bees.	E

2. Complete each sentence with a word from the list. Use a dictionary to help you.

invertebrate **symmetrical** **insect** **mollusk**

a) The human body is ______________________ because the left side of the body is a mirror image of the right side.

b) A spider does not have a backbone. It is classified as a(n) ___________________.

c) Butterflies are classified into the ______________________ group of invertebrates.

d) Snails and slugs are good examples of invertebrates. They are classified into th e ______________________ group of invertebrates.

NAME: ______________________

Invertebrates

We have already looked at **vertebrates**, the first of the two groups of higher animals. **Invertebrates** are the second group. Invertebrates' bodies are organized differently from vertebrates' bodies. They do not have backbones.

It is probably hard to imagine an animal that does not have a backbone. Can you believe that 98 percent of all animal species in the world are invertebrates? That means there are at least one million invertebrates that are living around us! Invertebrates are divided into groups: **insects** (butterflies, flies, bees), **mollusks** (snails, slugs), and **arachnids** (spiders).

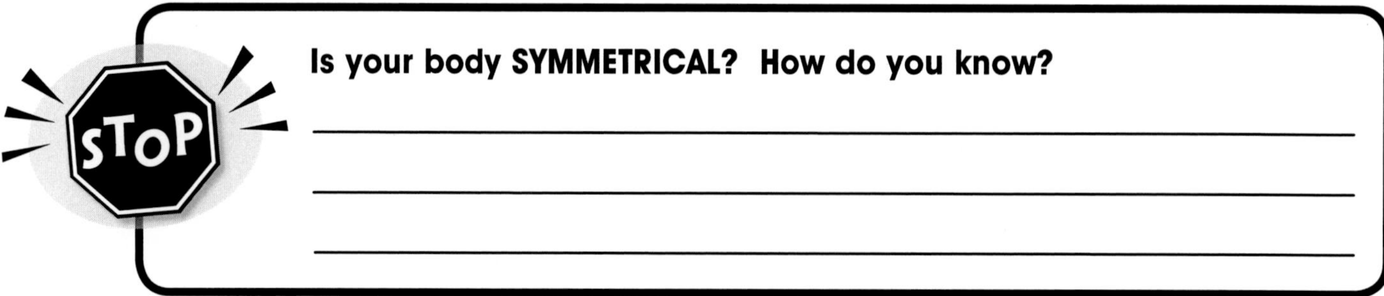

Is your body SYMMETRICAL? How do you know?

____

____

____

All invertebrates share common **features**. There are some important ones that help us classify animals as invertebrates. Let's look at the following features: Invertebrates do not have a backbone. This is how they got their name! "Invertebrate" means no vertebrae, no backbone. Invertebrates are multicellular. Cells in an invertebrate work together to help the organism survive. Each cell has specific duties and responsibilities. Most invertebrates reproduce sexually, not asexually. That means that a new organism is formed from male and female cells. Most invertebrates can move. The bodies of most invertebrates are **symmetrical**. Symmetrical means that if you draw a line down the middle, the left side would be the mirror image of the right side. Invertebrates can't make their own food. They feed off other things to get their energy.

NAME: ___________________________

Invertebrates

1. Put a check mark (✓) next to the answer that best finishes the sentence.

a) How do you know if an animal is an **invertebrate**?

- ◯ **A** It gets its energy from eating plants.
- ◯ **B** It does not have a backbone.
- ◯ **C** You can't tell if an animal is an invertebrate by looking at it.
- ◯ **D** It has a backbone.

b) What are the three groups that all invertebrates are divided into?

- ◯ **A** herbivores, carnivores, and omnivores
- ◯ **B** plants, animals, and fungi
- ◯ **C** reptiles, amphibians, and fish
- ◯ **D** insects, mollusks, and arachnids

c) What are three examples of insects?

- ◯ **A** butterflies, flies, and bees
- ◯ **B** ants, deer, and mice
- ◯ **C** bees, flies, and snails
- ◯ **D** snails, spiders, and slugs

d) What does it mean to be **symmetrical**?

- ◯ **A** You eat the same food as other organisms in your population.
- ◯ **B** The left side is a mirror image of the right side.
- ◯ **C** The left side looks the exact same as the right side.
- ◯ **D** The left side looks completely different from the right side.

e) Can invertebrates produce their own food?

- ◯ **A** Yes, they produce their own food through photosynthesis.
- ◯ **B** Yes, they produce their own food by using energy from the sun.
- ◯ **C** No, they can't make their own food. They feed off things to get their energy.
- ◯ **D** No, they can't make their own food. They do not need food to survive.

NAME: ______________________

Invertebrates

2. Use a dictionary to look up the definitions of MOLLUSK and ARACHNID. Write down the dictionary's definition, and then write your own definition of each word.

a) **mollusk** (dictionary): ______________________

b) **mollusk** (own definition): ______________________

c) **arachnid** (dictionary): ______________________

d) **arachnid** (own definition): ______________________

Extension and Application

3. Invent your own Invertebrate!

Ninety-eight percent of all animal species in the world are invertebrates! There are around one million invertebrates. Now you have the chance to add one more invertebrate to the list! Reread the section of the reading passage that lists the common features of invertebrates. Using this information, **invent your own invertebrate**. It is important that your animal has the typical invertebrate **features**. In this activity, you have the choice of either drawing a picture of your invertebrate invention or writing a story about it. In your answer, you will need to include the following:

- a name for your invertebrate invention
- a list of the features that classify it as an invertebrate

Use your imagination. Your invertebrate should not look like any animal you have ever seen before. Be creative!

4. Are Butterflies Symmetrical? Let's remind ourselves what it means if something is symmetrical. It means that if you drew a line down the middle of it, the left side would be the mirror image of the right side. Humans are symmetrical! Look at your two hands. They are mirror images of each other!

Butterflies are also symmetrical. In this activity, you will complete the butterfly drawing on the next page. You will see that the one side is already drawn. Knowing that the butterfly is symmetrical, you will be able to complete the other side. By the end, you should have two sides that are mirror images of each other. Use a pencil!

NAME: ____________________

Are Butterflies Symmetrical?

NAME: ______________________

Animal Adaptations

1. A HABITAT is the environment in which a plant or animal lives. In the first box, draw a picture of what you think a worm's habitat looks like. In the second box, draw a picture of what you think a fish's habitat looks like. Fill in the whole box!

A worm's habitat	A fish's habitat

2. Complete each sentence with a term from the list. Use a dictionary to help you.

habitat **physical features** **adaptation** **physical adaptation**

a) A(n) ____________________ is something that has been changed for a specific reason.

b) The environment in which a plant or animal lives is called a ____________________.

c) ________________________________ are things that describe an animal's body features.

d) A physical feature that has been changed for survival purposes is called a ________________________________.

NAME: ______________________

Animal Adaptations

All animals live in habitats. What is a **habitat**? A habitat is the **environment** in which a plant or animal lives. Habitats provide food, water and shelter. These are the things that animals need in order to survive. There is more to survival than just habitat though.

Animals also depend on their **physical features** for survival. These are things that describe the animal's body features you can see. Animals need to find food. They need to stay safe. They need to build homes. They need to survive bad weather. They need to attract mating partners. How do they do this? Animals depend on their physical features for these things. These are called **physical adaptations**. An adaptation is something that has been changed for a specific reason. Animals do not adapt their physical features over one lifetime. They do not develop their physical adaptations in a short period of time. Rather, their physical adaptations develop over many generations.

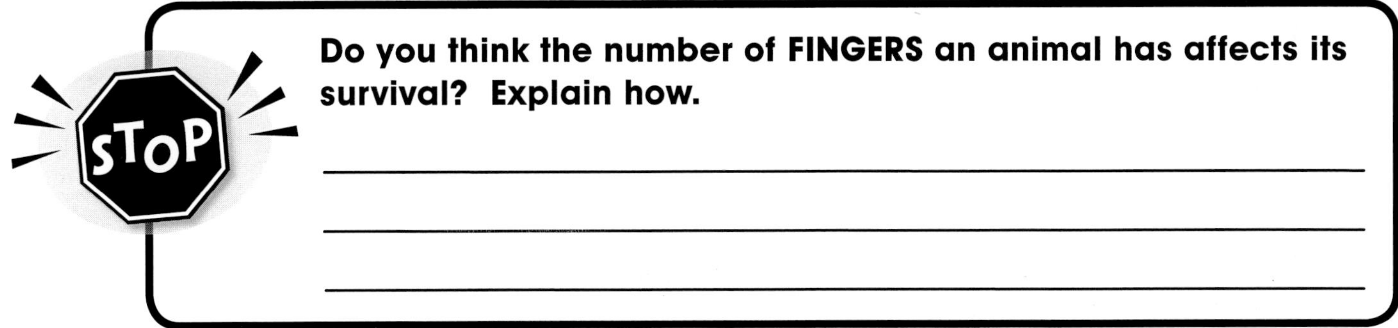

Do you think the number of FINGERS an animal has affects its survival? Explain how.

____

____

____

Let's look at some examples of physical adaptations which help different animals survive. The color of the fur, how thick or thin the fur is, the number of fingers, the shape of the nose or legs, and the shape of a bird's beak are all examples of physical adaptations. Can you name the animal in the picture above? If you said **koala** you are correct! The koala has one special physical adaptation that helps it live in a tree. Keep reading to find out what it is!

After You Read

NAME: ____________________

Animal Adaptations

1. **Circle the word True if the statement is true. Circle the word False if it is false.**

   a) The only two things that animals need to survive are food and water.

   True **False**

   b) Animals depend on their physical features for survival.

   True **False**

   c) Animals are able to adapt their physical features over one lifetime.

   True **False**

   d) The color of fur, and the shape of the nose are two examples of an animal's physical adaptations.

   True **False**

   e) Animals need to find food. They need to stay safe. They need to build homes.

   True **False**

2. **Write each word beside its meaning. There is ONE word that does NOT have a matching definition! Use the reading passage to write a definition for the remaining word.**

   habitat **environment** **physical feature** **adaptation** **physical adaptation**

   [ ] **a)** a physical feature that has been changed for survival purposes

   [ ] **b)** a feature that describes the animal's body features

   [ ] **c)** the environment in which a plant or animal lives

   [ ] **d)** something that has been changed for a specific reason

   [ ] **e)** ____________________.

NAME: ______________________________

Animal Adaptations

Answer the questions in complete sentences.

3. What is a **habitat**? Give two examples to support your answer.

____

4. How do animals depend on their physical features for survival?

____

5. Give an example of a **physical adaptation**. How would it help an animal survive in its habitat?

____

Extension and Application

6. Get Your Coupons Here... Physical Adaptations for a Low Price!

We have learned that animals do not develop their **physical adaptations** in a short period of time. Rather, their physical adaptations develop over many generations. For this activity however, we will pretend that animals will be able to buy their own physical adaptation. Yes, you will definitely need to use your imagination for this activity!

Gather information about 1 animal and its physical adaptations. You will use this information and **design a coupon** that you would see in a magazine or a newspaper. What is a **coupon**? It is a voucher that gives somebody a discount on something. Your coupon will not sell food or clothing. Instead, it will **sell physical adaptations to animals**. Include the following information on your coupon:

- A picture of the animal (either a drawing or a magazine clip)
- A slogan (The slogan should "sell" the adaptation. It should convince the animal who is going shopping that it should buy this physical adaptation! It should answer the question: *How does this adaptation help with survival?*)
- A price (how much is this physical adaptation going to cost the animal?)
- Information about the animal and what purpose this physical adaptation serves

Stretch your imagination and be as creative as possible!

NAME: ______________________________

A Case Study: The Koala and Its Adaptations

1. Draw a line from the word on the left to its matching definition. Which word is left over? Use the reading passage or a dictionary to help you write out its definition.

1	physical adaptation	the regular weather patterns of a place	A
2	marsupial	when a hand has a second thumb on it	B
3	climate	something that has been changed for a specific reason	C
4	opposable thumb	an animal that has a pouch on its front to carry its young	D
5	adaptation	______________________________ ______________________________	E

2. Look at the matched definitions in the question above. Use each vocabulary word in your own sentence. Make sure your sentence shows that you understand what the word means.

a) physical adaptation ______________________________

____

b) marsupial ______________________________

____

c) climate ______________________________

____

d) opposable thumb ______________________________

____

NAME: ______________________

A Case Study: The Koala and Its Adaptations

We read how animals depend on their physical features to help them survive in their environment. Do you remember what these physical features are called? **Physical adaptations**. Let's find out how the koala has adapted over time for its life in a tree. Before reading on, can you think of a physical feature that might help an animal live in a tree?

The koala is a medium-sized animal with thick, dense fur. Its fur is mainly gray. It looks like a cuddly teddy bear but it is actually a **marsupial**. What is a marsupial? A marsupial is an animal that has a pouch to carry its young. Can you think of another marsupial? Have you ever seen a kangaroo carrying its young in its front pouch?

Koalas live in hot and dry climates. A **climate** is the regular weather patterns of a place. Since koalas live in a hot climate, you would think they would need to drink a lot of water. They have adapted though by eating a lot of eucalyptus leaves. These leaves have so much water in them that koalas almost never need to drink! Did you know that the word "koala" is actually an aboriginal word meaning "no drink animal"?

Can you think of a physical feature that YOU have that helps you survive in your environment?

____

____

Koalas have adapted well to their life in a tree. They sleep for fourteen hours every day and then move from tree to tree at night. Their front paws have long, sharp claws. These help them climb from one tree to the next. Koalas also have another very special adaptation. They have an **opposable thumb**. Look at your own hands. You have one thumb. It would be very difficult to do things without your thumb. Koalas don't have one thumb. They have two! This gives them an excellent grip for their life in a tree.

NAME: ______________________________

The Koala and Its Adaptations

1. Circle the word True if the statement is true. Circle the word False if it is false.

a) The koala is an example of a marsupial because it carries its young in a pouch on the front of its body.

True **False**

b) A grizzly bear is another good example of a marsupial.

True **False**

c) Koalas need to drink a lot of water, so they live next to rivers and lakes.

True **False**

d) Long, sharp front claws help koalas climb trees. This is one of their physical adaptations.

True **False**

e) Koalas have an opposable thumb. Having a second thumb gives them excellent grip for their life in trees.

True **False**

2. Circle the answer that best completes each sentence.

a) Animals depend on their ______________________________ to help them survive in their environment.

physical energy **physical features**

b) A marsupial is an animal that has a __________________ to carry its young.

pouch **partner**

c) Koalas live in hot and dry climates. They have adapted well to their life in a __________________ .

desert **tree**

d) Koalas have an ____________________ thumb which gives them extra grip for swinging from tree to tree.

opposite **opposable**

NAME: ____________________

The Koala and Its Adaptations

Answer the questions in complete sentences.

3. What is a **marsupial**? Give two examples of marsupials.

____

4. How have koalas **adapted** to the hot and dry climates in which they live? Use examples from the reading passage.

____

____

5. What is an **opposable thumb**? Why is it such an important physical adaptation for the koala?

____

Extension and Application

6. Pin the Physical Adaptations on the Koala!

The koala has **many** physical adaptations that have developed over generations to help it survive in its environment. On the next page is a picture of a koala. Lines point to special physical features which have been adapted. Use research tools and the reading passage to **label** these adaptations.

Once you have completed the koala worksheet, you are ready to **choose your own animal**! Create a similar sheet for your own animal. This time you will need to draw your animal. Use a separate piece of paper. After you have drawn your animal, use lines and words to label its own physical adaptations.

By the end of this activity, you should have **two** drawings: the koala and the animal you have chosen.

7. What Does an Opposable Thumb Look Like?

In this activity, you will gather information about the opposable thumb. What is it? What does it look like? What purpose does it serve? You will answer these questions using a format of your choice. Present your information in a fun and creative way. You could put a presentation together, write a newspaper article, design a brochure, etc. It is up to you! Be creative!

NAME: ______________________

Pin the Physical Adaptations on the Koala!

NAME: ______________________________

Evolution and the Fossil Record

1. EVOLUTION is the change of POPULATIONS of living organisms over time. Humans have evolved too. It is widely believed that humans evolved from the ape. In the boxes below, draw what you think the different stages of human evolution might look like. The first drawing (the ape) and the last drawing (the human) have been done for you.

2. Complete each sentence with a word from the list. Use a dictionary to help you.

evolution **fossil** **sedimentary rock** **paleontologist**

a) A ______________________ is a scientist that studies fossils.

b) The remains of an animal or plant that are preserved from a long time ago are called a ______________________.

c) ______________________________ is a kind of rock made of hardened layers of gravel, sand and mud. Fossils are often found in this kind of rock.

d) ______________________ is the change of populations of living organisms over time.

NAME: ____________________

Evolution and the Fossil Record

When was the last time you saw a dinosaur running across the street? Dinosaurs no longer exist. Today, other animals exist, doing the same things that dinosaurs used to do, search for food. Birds fly in the skies, fish swim in the oceans, and bears crawl on the land. Life on Earth has changed over time. This is called **evolution**. Evolution is the change of populations of living organisms over time.

Scientists have been collecting information and evidence of evolution for over 300 years. You might wonder how scientists can learn about life from so long ago when cameras and news clips didn't exist. Scientists gathered a lot of information by studying **fossils**. What is a fossil? A fossil is the remains of an animal or plant that are preserved from a long time ago. A scientist that studies fossils is called a **paleontologist** – that's a big word! These remains are found inside a rock.

Have you ever picked up a rock and found a PATTERN on it? Describe what it looked like.

____

____

The **fossil record** is the most accurate way to study past life on Earth. The fossil record clearly shows changes in life through layers of **sedimentary rock**. Sedimentary rock is made of layers of gravel, sand and mud (sediment) that have collected over time. Bits and pieces of living things are trapped in between these layers. Over time, the layers of sediment are flattened down and eventually harden and form sedimentary rock. The buried plant and animal remains become fossils within the sedimentary layers.

NAME: ______________________

Evolution and the Fossil Record

1. Put a check mark (✓) next to the answer that best finishes the sentence.

a) Scientists have been collecting information and evidence of evolution for...

- ○ **A** scientists do not study evolution.
- ○ **B** the last ten years.
- ○ **C** as long as life forms have existed.
- ○ **D** over 300 years.

b) Evolution is the change of populations of...

- ○ **A** human beings over generations.
- ○ **B** living organisms over time.
- ○ **C** plants who live longer than 100 years.
- ○ **D** living organisms over a period of 1 year.

c) An effective way to study evolution is to...

- ○ **A** read news reports that discuss important events.
- ○ **B** look at pictures drawn by people who lived on Earth hundreds of years ago.
- ○ **C** study animal or plant remains found in rock, called fossils.
- ○ **D** study rocks and minerals.

d) The fossil record is the most accurate way to study past life on Earth. It shows...

- ○ **A** changes in life through layers of sedimentary rock.
- ○ **B** all the fossils that scientists have found in the last 100 years.
- ○ **C** plants and animals that live so long that they form into rock.
- ○ **D** animals only, and what their ancestors looked like.

2. Circle the word True if the statement's true. Circle the word False if it's false.

a) Evolution is the change of populations of non-living things over time.

True **False**

b) Life on Earth has not changed. It is the same as it was thousands of years ago.

True **False**

c) Paleontologists are scientists that study fossils to find out more about evolution.

True **False**

d) Plant and animal remains buried in sedimentary rock become fossils within the sedimentary layers.

True **False**

After You Read

NAME: ____________________

Evolution and the Fossil Record

3. Use a dictionary to look up the definition of FOSSIL and EVOLUTION. Write down the dictionary's definitions. Then write a sentence using each word that shows the meaning of the word.

a) fossil (dictionary): ____________________

b) fossil (own definition): ____________________

c) evolution (dictionary): ____________________

d) evolution (own definition): ____________________

Extension and Application

4. Uncover the Fossil!

Below is a picture of a fossil. This fossil shows the remains of an animal that has been preserved from a long time ago. Pretend you are a scientist. What can you tell from looking at the picture? Use you imagination to come up with a story about this animal. While writing your story, think about the following questions: What was life like for this animal? What did it eat? Where did it live? How did it survive?

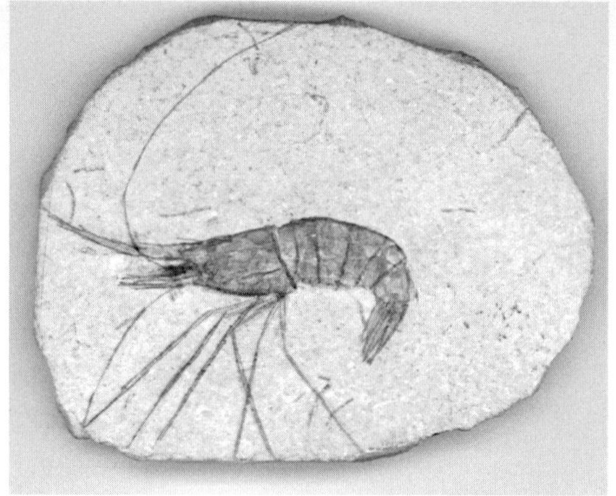

5. Write Your Own Job Description!

You have been hired by the State research lab to be their new paleontologist! You have an important job to do! A paleontologist is a scientist that studies fossils and evolution. Many people are relying on you to uncover important information about life on Earth and how it has changed over time. Use research tools (internet, encyclopedia, books) to find out more about what a paleontologist does. Once you have collected enough information, write your own job description. After you have written it, share it with a partner. He or she should be able to get a good impression of what your job is all about!

Brush Up on Your Classifying Skills!

Let's remind ourselves what it means to **classify** something: to divide things into groups based on similarities. This makes it easier for us to study things.

In this activity, you will brush up on your own classifying skills!

Look through a magazine and cut out the first **ten** pictures you see of an **animal**. Look for pictures showing many different animals: big, small, fury, frightening looking, slimy, etc.

Can you think of any other adjectives to describe animals?

Once you have cut out your ten pictures, arrange the pictures on a piece of paper. You are ready to brainstorm how you are going to classify your animals. You are going to divide your group of animals into small groups.

How are you going to divide up the animals? Look for **similarities** and **differences** between the animals. Here's a clue: you've already read some ideas of how you can classify animals earlier in this question!

Using a large piece of Bristol board, present your classification. Display your classification groups in a creative way.

On your Bristol board, you should include the following:

- **A title**
- **Glued on images of the ten animals (organized in their groups)**
- **Labels showing how you have classified the animals**
- **A half-page write-up explaining how you classified your animals**

How Important Are Thumbs?

The goal of this activity is to provide you with a chance to understand how important the thumb is for animals. You will discover:

- which of your simple daily activities are possible only because of your thumbs
- which activities take longer without the use of a thumb
- what sort of human activities would not be possible to do without your thumbs

Materials: (per group)

masking tape, scissors, paper clips, zip-lock bag, plastic fork and knife, pencil, paper, balloons

Instructions:

1. Tape your thumbs to the sides of your hands.
2. Then, try to complete the tasks that are listed below. Be careful not to use your thumbs! After completing each item, write out the answers to the following questions:

   A. Is the task more difficult with or without a thumb?

   B. How did you have to change your usual technique in order to complete this task?

   C. Do you think organisms without thumbs would carry out this task on a regular basis? Why or why not?

Tasks:

- Pick up a pen or pencil from the table. Use it to write your name on paper.
- Open a book. Turn a few pages, one page at a time.
- Pick up a piece of chalk. Write your name on the board.
- Tear off a small piece of tape.
- Turn on the water faucet. Turn it off.
- Sharpen a pencil.
- Cut a circle out of a piece of paper using scissors.
- Pick up one paper clip. Clip a pile of papers together.
- Tie your shoelaces.
- Button several buttons.
- Zip up your jacket.
- Blow up a balloon and tie it.
- Close a zip-lock bag.

The Lake Habitat Thermometer

For this activity, you will need:
- A thermometer
- The picture of the "Lake Habitat"

Look at the picture of the "Lake Habitat".
Then read the following description of it:

The current temperature of the air is 47 degrees F.
The highest temperature of the water is 37 degrees F.
The temperature of the soil is 49 degrees F.
The date is January 9. The time is late afternoon.
And the sky is very cloudy.

While you are reading the above description, look at your **thermometer**. Can you find the above temperatures on your thermometer? Work with a partner if you are having trouble.

In your notebook, copy down the following questions. Answer them using what you have learned about warm-blooded and cold-blooded animals.

Questions:

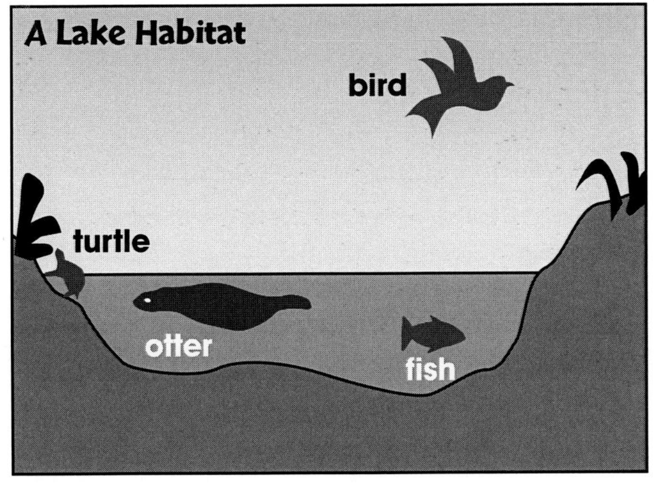

1. Approximately what is the body temperature of the fish?
2. Approximately what is the body temperature of the otter?
3. Approximately what is the body temperature of the bird?
4. Is there anything the fish can do to increase its body temperature to much more than about 37 degrees F?
5. How well is the otter insulated in the cold winter?
6. How well is the fish insulated?
7. If an animal is poorly insulated, what is the disadvantage in cold weather?

A Day in the Life of a Paleontologist!

In this activity, you will pretend you a paleontologist and head out into the field! Your 'field' for this activity will be the schoolyard. In groups of 3 or 4, you will investigate what life is in your schoolyard. You might not find fossils from 500 years ago, but you will definitely find something to give you a glimpse of <u>evolution</u> in the schoolyard.

On your trip, you will need to bring the following:

- Pencil
- Paper (for recording what you find, and where you found it)
- A bucket or container to collect rocks
- Digging tool (small shovel or sandbox shovel)

When you are out in the schoolyard, pick an area that is going to be your **dig site**. Don't pick too large an area – you don't want to dig up too much of the playground!

Look for rocks and stones that appear different from typical, round and smooth rocks. Look for patterns, lines, different textures, etc.

Once you have collected enough evidence on your dig, return to the classroom and record your observations. In your notebook, **write up a report** answering the following questions:

- **Where in the schoolyard did you carry out your 'dig'?**
- **What kind of vegetation was there at your dig site? (grass, gravel, etc.)**
- **Did you find any rocks that looked interesting? Describe them.**
- **Did you find any rocks that had a pattern on them?**
- **What did the patterns look like?**
- **Do you think you found a fossil?**

Once you have answered these questions, **draw a picture** showing you working at your dig site. Next to this picture, draw a picture of all the items (for example, rocks) that you found at your dig site.

NAME: ______________________________

Crossword Puzzle!

Across

1 when things are divided into groups based on similarities

5 a person who studies living things

7 describes an animal that is able to stay at the same body temperature

9 a single organism

10 the surroundings where an animal lives

12 a scientist that studies fossils

Down

1 an animal that cannot control their own body temperature

2 describes something where the left side is the mirror image of the right side

3 a living thing such as a plant or animal

4 a physical feature that has been changed for survival purposes

6 the group of invertebrates including snails and slugs

8 the change of populations of living organisms over time

11 an animal that has a backbone

13 energy that comes from the sun

14 the remains of an animal or plant that are preserved

1 2 3 4 5 6 7 8 9 10 11 12 13 14

After You Read

NAME: ____________________

Word Search

Find all of the words in the Word Search. Words may be horizontal, vertical, or diagonal. A few may even be backwards! Look carefully!

classification	class	invertebrate	habitat
organism	family	nerve	adaptation
sense	species	tissue	marsupial
biologist	coldblooded	insect	opposable
category	warmblooded	mollusk	evolution
kingdom	environment	arachnid	fossil
phylum	vertebrate	symmetrical	paleontologist

p	c	v	r	f	g	s	e	i	c	e	p	s	w	q	k	o	b
h	w	a	r	m	b	l	o	o	d	e	d	y	s	a	c	p	i
y	e	v	o	l	u	t	i	o	n	n	y	m	d	z	a	p	o
l	w	f	s	w	e	t	l	l	n	v	h	m	n	r	t	o	l
u	d	r	a	u	r	v	x	a	h	i	n	e	e	t	e	s	o
m	v	a	z	m	w	y	u	j	g	r	t	t	r	y	g	a	g
s	e	c	e	g	i	f	h	k	f	o	g	r	v	h	o	b	i
r	r	v	d	f	g	l	m	y	r	n	b	i	e	d	r	l	s
t	t	b	n	m	j	g	y	t	e	m	r	c	w	f	y	e	t
y	e	d	i	n	h	c	a	r	a	e	f	a	d	h	h	f	d
u	b	m	q	s	v	b	m	u	y	n	v	l	x	b	y	r	w
l	r	m	a	z	x	c	v	b	g	t	m	o	d	g	n	i	k
c	a	a	o	r	i	n	v	e	r	t	e	b	r	a	t	e	d
l	t	s	l	l	s	a	s	d	f	g	f	s	h	f	s	n	e
a	e	d	k	e	l	u	w	e	r	t	o	m	a	y	r	f	d
s	h	f	j	d	f	u	p	r	t	y	s	s	b	k	t	m	o
s	e	n	s	e	g	j	s	i	o	u	s	i	i	y	t	e	o
d	f	g	h	j	h	j	k	k	a	l	i	n	t	w	i	y	l
a	d	a	p	t	a	t	i	o	n	l	l	a	a	h	s	q	b
t	c	e	s	n	i	a	s	d	f	g	m	g	t	f	s	e	d
q	w	e	r	t	y	u	l	o	p	l	n	r	f	d	u	w	l
c	l	a	s	s	i	f	i	c	a	t	i	o	n	z	e	b	o
p	a	l	e	o	n	t	o	l	o	g	i	s	t	w	y	p	c

NAME: ______________________

Comprehension Quiz

Part A

Circle the word True if the statement is true. Circle the word False if it is false.

1. To classify something means to divide things into groups based on similarities.
   True **False**
2. Biologists are scientists who study evolution and fossils.
   True **False**
3. The difference between warm-blooded and cold-blooded animals is their ability to control their own body temperature.
   True **False**
4. There are more invertebrates living on Earth than vertebrates.
   True **False**
5. Invertebrates are organized the same way as vertebrates. They also have a backbone.
   True **False**
6. Animals adapt their physical features over long periods of time so that they survive in their habitat.
   True **False**
7. The koala has an opposable thumb on each hand which gives it excellent grip for swinging in trees.
   True **False**
8. Scientists study evolution by reading newspaper reports from hundreds of years ago. These reports show how life on Earth has changed over time.
   True **False**

Part B

Label each picture below as either a **vertebrate** or an **invertebrate.**

a) ______________ **b)** ______________ **c)** ______________

SUBTOTAL: /14

After You Read

NAME: ____________________

Comprehension Quiz

Part C

Answer the questions in complete sentences.

1. What is the difference between a **warm-blooded animal** and a **cold-blooded animal**? 2

____

____

2. What does it mean to **classify** something? Give an example to support your answer. 2

____

____

3. Why are **vertebrates** called "the most advanced organism on Earth"? 2

____

____

____

4. What is a **physical adaptation**? Use information you have learned about the **koala** to support your answer. 2

____

____

5. What is **evolution**? How do scientists gather information about **evolution**? 2

____

____

____

SUBTOTAL: /10

NAME: ______________________________

What Is a Cell?

1. Fill in each blank with a word from the list below. You may use a dictionary to help.

Matter **cell** **magnify** **microscope** **organism** **building block**

a) If something is too small to see, you can use a(n) [ ] to magnify it.

b) A(n) [ ] is a living thing such as a plant or animal.

c) To [ ] something means to make it look larger than it really is.

d) A piece of an object whose job is to help the object grow is called a(n) [ ].

e) [ ] is anything that has mass and takes up space.

f) The smallest unit of living matter is called a(n) [ ].

2. List what you think are the BUILDING BLOCKS in each of the following things. The first one is done for you as an example. There might be more than one building block. List only one!

a) A brick house: The building block is a **single piece of brick.**

b) A sand castle: The building block is ______________________________.

c) A stack of pancakes: The building block is ______________________________.

d) A pad of paper: The building block is ______________________________.

e) A piece of paper (a tricky one!): The building block is ______________________________.

f) A Lego hospital: The building block is ______________________________.

g) A pile of laundry: The building block is ______________________________.

Reading Passage

NAME: ____________________

What Is a Cell?

Did you know that your own body is made up of millions and millions of impossible-to-see things called **cells**? Even if you tried, you could not count the number of cells in your body. There are too many! Did you know that these millions of cells all came from one tiny cell? They all came from the first tiny cell that was you! Every living thing on Earth began life as one tiny cell like you did. Worms, monkeys, zebras and spiders all began as one tiny cell. What are cells though?

When you were smaller, did you ever build something out of Lego or blocks? Think of each piece of Lego or block as a cell. So, we can say that cells are the **building blocks** of life. A cell is so tiny that if you want to see it, you will need to use a very powerful microscope. A **microscope** uses a lens to **magnify** what you are trying to see. To magnify something makes it look much bigger than it really is. A single cell is very tiny. If a cell was big enough to see with just your eyes, you would be as big as the Empire State Building!

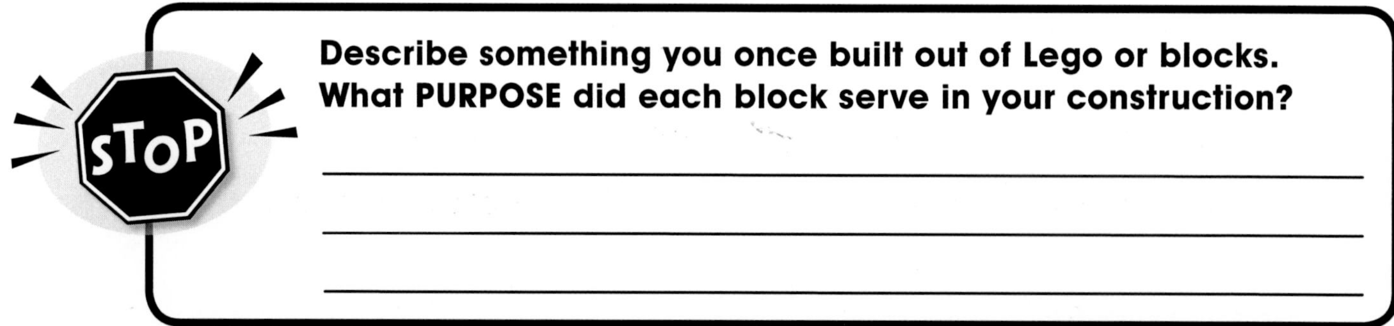

Describe something you once built out of Lego or blocks. What PURPOSE did each block serve in your construction?

____

____

____

A cell is the smallest unit of living matter. **Matter** is anything that has mass and takes up space. All **organisms**, including plants and animals, are made up of cells. There are many different kinds of cells. They all have different shapes, sizes and jobs to do. As we know with humans, most organisms are made up of millions of cells. There are also some organisms which are made up of only one cell. We will learn about these in the next section.

NAME: ______________________________

What Is a Cell?

1. Circle the word True if the statement is true. Circle the word False if it's false.

a) All the cells in turkeys, dogs and flowers started as one tiny cell.

True **False**

b) If you look very closely, you would be able to see a few cells that are in your body.

True **False**

c) A microscope helps you see things that are so big you cannot see them when you are standing still.

True **False**

d) A cell is the absolute smallest unit of living matter.

True **False**

e) There are many different kinds of cells, but they all are exactly the same shape and size.

True **False**

2. Circle the answer that best completes each sentence.

a) Matter is anything that has ______________ and takes up space.

energy **mass**

b) A cell is so tiny that you need to use a ______________ if you want to see it.

microscope **magnifying glass**

c) Everything living on Earth began life as one tiny ______________.

person **cell**

After You Read

NAME: ______________________

What Is a Cell?

Answer the questions in complete sentences.

3. What is a **cell**?

____

4. Can you see a cell with just your eyes? What do you need to use in order to see a cell? Use terms from the reading passage in your answer.

____

5. Do **all** cells look the same? How might cells be different from each other?

____

Extension and Application

6. Pretend you are a LEGO PIECE!

You are part of a construction that a child is building.

Describe what your job is as a Lego piece. In this activity, think of building blocks as part of the Lego building. In your response, be sure to answer these questions:

- What is your job?
- Who do you work with?
- How do you depend on others?
- How do others depend on you?
- What would happen if you (the Lego piece) did not exist?

7. How does a CELL PHONE work? Are **cells** only found in plants and animals? Did you know that the word "cell" in "cell phone" is a short form of the word "cellular"?

You are an electronic researcher. Your task is to prepare a report on how **cell phones** work. Pretend that the person who will read your report knows very little about what a cell is, or how a phone works. Use various research tools such as the Internet or an encyclopedia to find information on this topic. Use your imagination to present it in a creative way!

NAME: ______________________________

Single-celled & Multicellular Organisms

1. Draw a line from the word on the left to its matching definition. Which word is left over? Use the reading passage or a dictionary to help you write out its definition.

1	organism	The structure in the middle of the cell	A
2	amoeba	Something in a cell that carries genetic information	B
3	multicellular	Describes an organism that is made up of only one cell	C
4	single-celled	A simple, yet complicated, single-celled organism	D
5	nucleus	A small structure in multicellular organisms that carries out day-to-day cell operations	E
6	DNA	Describes an organism that is made up of many cells	F
7	organelle	______________________________ ______________________________	G

2. In the space below, draw what you think a cell might look like. If the nucleus is in the middle of the cell, what do you think it would look like?

NAME: ______________________

Single-celled & Multicellular Organisms

Do you remember how your body is made up of millions and millions of tiny things called cells? We cannot even count the number of cells in our body. Humans are therefore **multicellular organisms**. Multicellular organisms are living things that are made up of more than one cell. Most things you can think of are multicellular organisms. A tree, a monkey, and a fish are all examples of multicellular organisms.

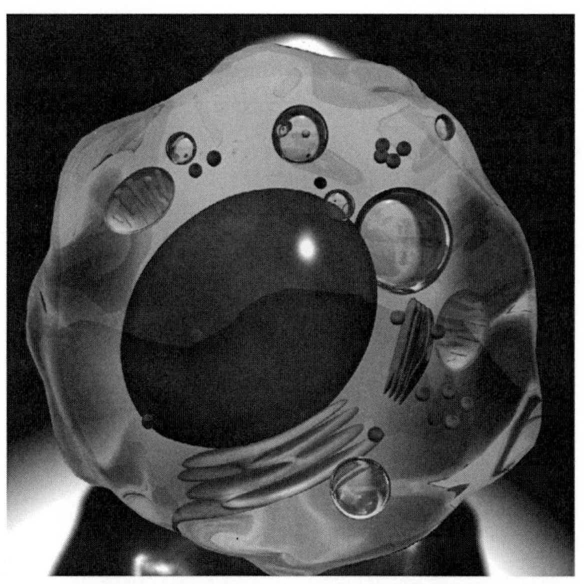

You probably would not believe it, but there are some living things that are made up of only one tiny cell! We call these living things **single-celled organisms**. **Amoeba** and bacteria are both examples of single-celled organisms. You might think these organisms are simple. They are more complex than you think! An **amoeba** is a single-celled organism that lives in the ocean, in fresh water, in soil and even inside the bodies of large animals! Some of these organisms even live in our mouths and digestive systems!

Describe what you think a SINGLE-CELLED ORGANISM might look like if you could see it with your own eyes.

____

____

____

NAME: ____________________

Single-celled & Multicellular Organisms

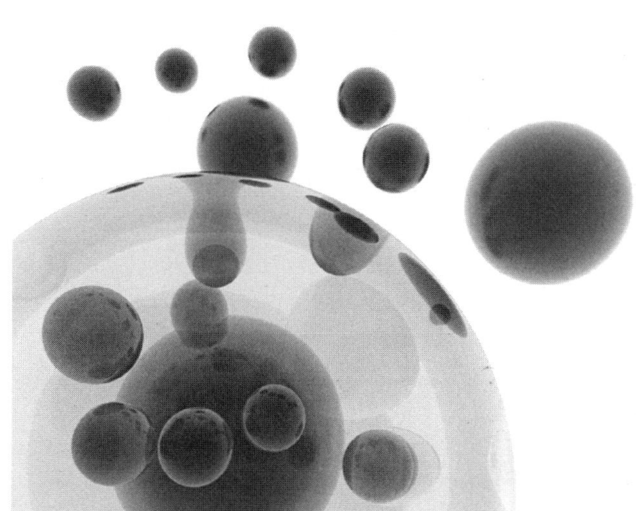

Single-celled organisms do not have a definite shape but they all have similar characteristics. In the middle of the cell is the **nucleus**. The nucleus is like a company's head office. It organizes all the activities in the cell. Around the nucleus is **protoplasm**. Protoplasm is a complicated structure that has many jobs to do. It consists of a double-layered membrane that is always changing.

Most living things are too large to be formed by just one single cell. These **multicellular organisms** are made up of many cells that live and work together. These cells each have their own job to do. The one characteristic that all cells in multicellular organisms have is a **nucleus**. They have a nucleus just like single-celled organisms do. In a multicellular organism, each cell's nucleus holds the cell's **DNA**. DNA is something that is small, yet complicated. It is the cell's genetic information. Another characteristic of multicellular organisms is that they have **organelles**. Organelles are small structures that help carry out day-to-day operations of the cell.

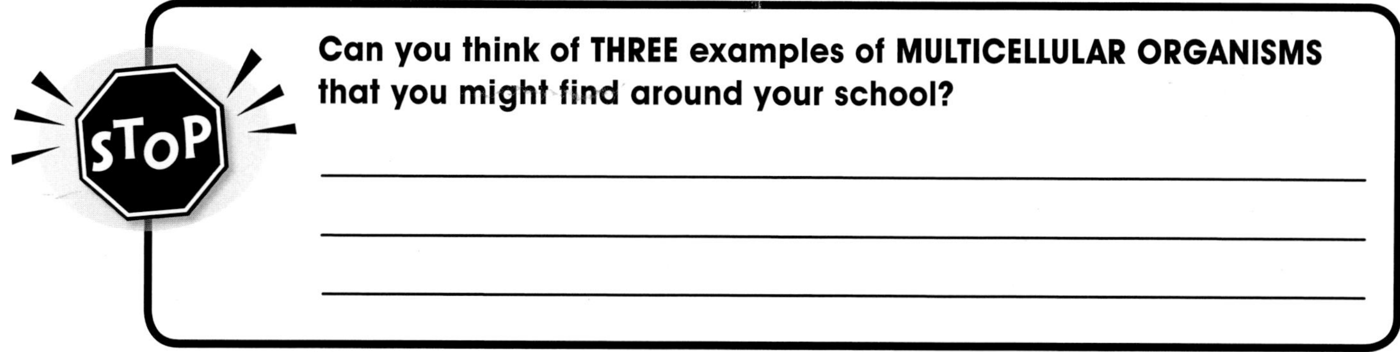

Can you think of THREE examples of MULTICELLULAR ORGANISMS that you might find around your school?

____

____

____

Most living things that you can see with your own eyes are multicellular organisms. This includes animals and plants. It is important not to forget the complicated, yet tiny, single-celled organisms though!

After You Read

NAME: ______________________

Single-celled & Multicellular Organisms

1. Put a check mark (✓) next to the answer that best finishes the sentence.

a) Your body is made up of millions and millions of...

- ○ **A** small pores in your skin.
- ○ **B** veins and arteries.
- ○ **C** tiny things called cells.
- ○ **D** proteins and sugars.

b) A tree, a monkey, and a fish are all examples of...

- ○ **A** organisms that produce their own food.
- ○ **B** living things that need very little oxygen to breathe.
- ○ **C** microscopic forms of life.
- ○ **D** multicellular organisms.

c) The word AMOEBA describes a...

- ○ **A** life form that is easily visible with your eyes.
- ○ **B** single-celled organism that lives in the ocean, in fresh water, or soil.
- ○ **C** an animal that has millions of cells in it.
- ○ **D** the dark center of a cell.

d) A multicellular organism's genetic information (DNA) is found in...

- ○ **A** the area just outside of the cell wall.
- ○ **B** the cell's nucleus, the center of the cell.
- ○ **C** all areas of the cell, wherever there is room for it.
- ○ **D** the organism's heart and lungs.

2. Circle the word True if the statement is true. Circle the word False if it's false.

a) Multicellular organisms are living things that are made up of exactly one cell.

True **False**

b) There is no organism that is made up of only one tiny cell.

True **False**

c) Single-celled organisms do not have a definite shape but they all have similar characteristics.

True **False**

d) Not all cells in multicellular organisms have a nucleus.

True **False**

NAME: ______________________________

After You Read

Single-celled & Multicellular Organisms

Answer each question with a complete sentence.

3. What is the difference between a single-celled organism and a multicellular organism?

____

4. Why is the nucleus in a single-celled organism important?

____

5. Multicellular organisms have **organelles**. What are they? What do they do?

____

Extension and Application

6. You are an AMOEBA living inside an elephant's body!

You are a single-celled organism that lives inside an elephant! Using information from the reading passage and other research tools, **write a story** about what your life is like. In your story include answers to these questions:

- What is a single-celled organism?
- Where do you live?
- What are the different parts of your cell?
- What jobs do these cell parts have?

Be creative. Once you have written your story, read it aloud to your classmates. Make it interesting. Use as many describing words as you can!

7. A Bubble Chart about DNA

You have been hired as the country's leading scientist to work on a project. Congratulations! Your job is to lead a research team to find out more information about DNA. DNA is a cell's genetic information. Pretend the science world knows very little about DNA. What research can you find on DNA?

First collect as much information as you can find using various research tools (library books, Internet, etc.) **List** the information in your notes and then organize the facts using the **Brainstorming Organizer** on the following page. Record one fact about DNA in each bubble.

After You Read

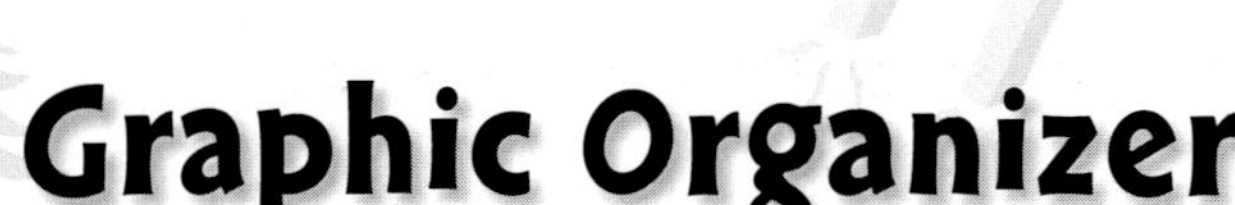

NAME: ______________________

Graphic Organizer

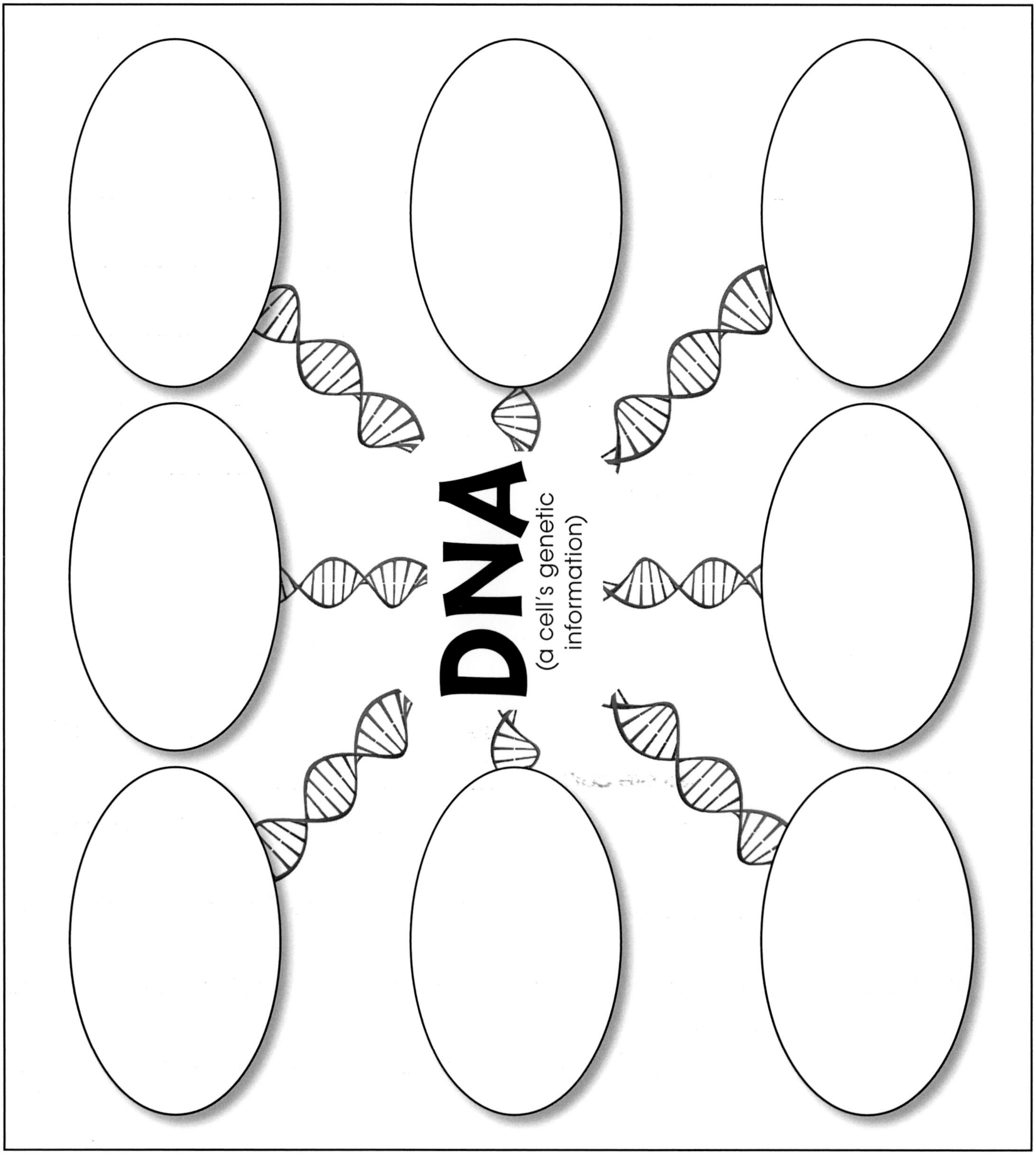
DNA
(a cell's genetic information)

NAME: ______________________________

The Parts of a Cell

1. You will be reading about the different parts of a cell. List as many different parts of the HUMAN BODY as you can think of. Can you think of at least TEN?

______________________ ______________________

______________________ ______________________

______________________ ______________________

______________________ ______________________

______________________ ______________________

______________________ ______________________

2. Complete each sentence with a word from the list. Use a dictionary to help you.

cell membrane **nucleus** **cell** **cytoplasm** **organelles** **cilia**

a) ____________________ is the jelly-like substance that fills the inside of the cell.

b) "Small organs" of a cell are called ____________________.

c) ____________________ are stick-like things that push cells around and make them move.

d) The ____________________ is the outside covering of the cell, very similar to our skin!

e) The center part of a cell that has other things grouped or built around it is called a(n) ____________________.

f) A(n) ____________________ is the smallest life form that can live on its own. It is tiny.

NAME: ______________________________

The Parts of a Cell

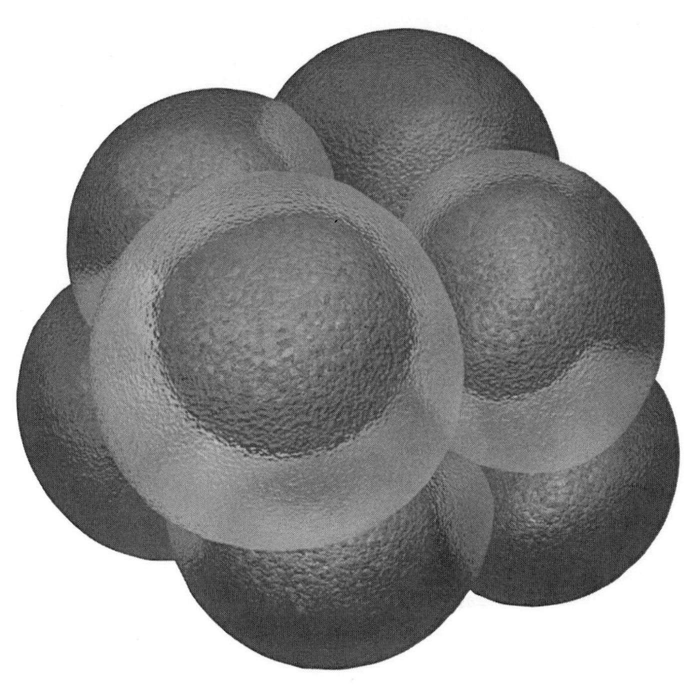

We now know that cells are different sizes and shapes. They all have different jobs to do, too. We read about how tiny the cells in our body are. But have you ever seen an ostrich's egg yolk? It is much bigger than the one in your sunny-side-up breakfast! It is the biggest cell that exists!

Even though cells all look different, they have some parts in common. All cells have an outside covering. This is called the **cell membrane**. Its job is similar to that of our skin. It surrounds the cell and holds the other parts of the cell in place. In general, the cell membrane protects the cell. Although it is strong, the cell membrane lets **particles** pass in and out of it.

Inside a cell's membrane are a nucleus and cytoplasm. The **nucleus** is the dark part located in the middle of the cell. Just like you have a brain, so does a cell! The nucleus is the cell's "brain". It controls everything that happens in the cell. Every cell is filled a jelly-like substance, called **cytoplasm**. It "listens" to the nucleus and it is where all the cell's activities take place.

A cell's nucleus controls everything that happens in the cell. What part of the human body is the nucleus SIMILAR to?

____

____

How do cells move? Many cells move with the help of cilia. **Cilia** are short stick-like things which act as "paddles". These paddles push the cells around and make them move. All of the small structures that are found inside a cell are called **organelles**. They are the "small organs" of the cell, just like we have our own organs in our body.

NAME: ______________________________

The Parts of a Cell

1. Circle the answer that best completes each sentence.

a) All cells have an outside covering, called a cell ________________.

boundary **membrane**

b) A cell membrane lets ________________ pass in and out of it.

particles **chemicals**

c) **Cytoplasm** is a jelly-like substance that fills the ________________ of a cell.

inside **outside**

d) **Cilia** are short stick-like things which act as ________________ to make cells move.

stoppers **paddles**

e) A(n) ________________ egg yolk is the biggest cell that exists.

chicken's **ostrich's**

2. Circle the word True if the statement is true. Circle the word False if it's false.

a) Cells are all different sizes and shapes, with different jobs to do.

True **False**

b) The cell membrane's job is to keep harmful things from entering the cell.

True **False**

c) A cell membrane is so strong that it does not let anything pass through it.

True **False**

d) The nucleus in a cell is see-through. Therefore, it does not have an important job to do.

True **False**

e) Organelles are small structures found inside a cell. They are the "small organs" of the cell.

True **False**

NAME: ______________________

The Parts of a Cell

3. Pick TWO cell parts from the following list:

cell membrane **cytoplasm** **nucleus** **cilia** **organelles**

Answer the following questions:

- What does the cell part look like, or where in the cell can it be found?
- What is the function of this cell part?

a) cell part: ______________________

looks like/where: ______________________

function: ______________________

b) cell part: ______________________

looks like/where: ______________________

function: ______________________

Extension and Application

4. Draw a cell's canoe route!
Cilia are stick-like things which act as **"paddles"**. They push cells around and make them move. On a blank piece of paper, draw a picture of a canoe and a person paddling in it. Pretend the canoe is the cell and the paddle is making a cell move. **Use your imagination** to draw what you think a cell's **"canoe route"** might be.

A few questions to consider:

- What does the cell look like?
- What do other cells look like?
- When the cell moves, what things does it move around?

5. A conversation between a nucleus and a cell membrane!
Pretend you hear a conversation between a **nucleus** and a **cell membrane**. They are discussing what they look like, where they are found in a cell, and what their important jobs are.

Using a dialogue structure (see below), write out their conversation.

NUCLEUS says: ______________________
CELL MEMBRANE says: ______________________
(Repeat order to continue conversation…)

NAME: ______________________________

What Cells Do

1. Fill in each blank with a word from the list. You may use a dictionary to help.

nucleus **cytoplasm** **cell membrane** **cell specialization**

specialize **multicellular organism**

a) An organism that is made up of more than one cell is called a

______________________________.

b) To ____________________ in something means to devote time only to one particular interest or skill.

c) The ________________ is the center of the cell, and directs all the cellular activities.

d) When a cell carries out a specific function, it is called

____.

e) The outside covering of a cell is called the ____________________.

f) ____________________ is a jelly-like substance that fills the inside of a cell.

2. Write the JOB that each of the following things has. Give an example of each to explain your answer.

a) A factory: ____

____

b) A factory boss: ____

____

c) A power source ____

____

d) A front door: ____

____

Reading Passage

NAME: ______________________

What Cells Do

Guess whose job it is to keep us alive and healthy? You may think our heart is what keeps us alive. This is a very important organ, but something else is important, too. If you could look on a smaller scale inside your body, you would see that our cells keep us alive.

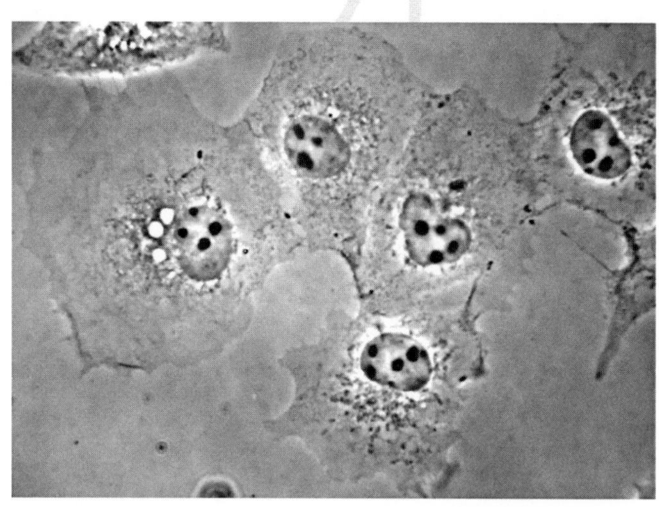

(Kidney cells)

Try to think of a cell as a tiny factory. Within the factory there are many parts, or structures, that work together. These parts let the factory run smoothly. Would a real factory be productive if people didn't show up for work? Parts of a cell must also work together for it to work smoothly and to keep the organism alive. The cell "factory" has a "boss" (**nucleus**) who directs all the cell's activities. It also has a "power source" (**cytoplasm**) which provides energy to carry out these activities. It also has a "front door" (**cell membrane**) that controls which materials can go in and out of the cell.

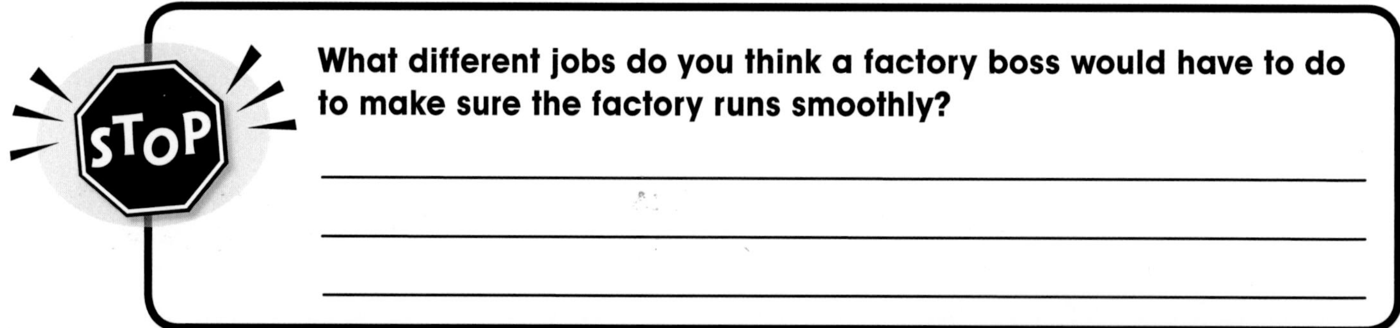

What different jobs do you think a factory boss would have to do to make sure the factory runs smoothly?

____

____

____

Now let's look at **cell specialization**. When a person is **specialized** in something, it means they have a unique and special **function**. They have their own job to do. Cells do too! Most multicellular organisms are made up of many specialized cells. This means that different cells carry out different functions to help keep the organism alive. Each cell has its own job, but they must still work together as a "team". For example, liver cells need other cells in the body (blood cells) to feed them oxygen and nutrients. So, both liver cells and blood cells work together as a team. Some specialized cells store food. Some carry nutrients to other cells. But remember that no matter what their job is, cells all have one main job: to keep the plant or animal alive.

NAME: ______________________

What Cells Do

1. Circle the word True if the statement is true. Circle the word False if it's false.

a) Cells all have different jobs to do, but their main job is to keep the organism alive.

True **False**

b) Parts of a cell do not have to work together. As long as they do their own job, the organism will survive.

True **False**

c) The cell's nucleus is like a front door. It controls what materials can go in and out of the cell.

True **False**

d) Each cell carries out a special function to help keep the organism alive. This is called cell specialization.

True **False**

e) Storing food and carrying nutrients are both examples of how cells are specialized.

True **False**

2. Write each word beside its meaning. There is ONE word that does NOT have a matching definition! Use the reading passage to write a definition for the remaining word.

cytoplasm **nucleus** **cell membrane** **cell specialization**

[ ] **a)** This is the dark center of a cell. It acts as the cell's brain.

[ ] **b)** A jelly-like substance found inside the walls of a cell.

[ ] **c)** Cells carry out their own special functions. In this way they help keep the organism alive.

[ ] **d)** ____.

NAME: ______________________

What Cells Do

3. a) Circle the term that describes the job of a **nucleus**:

power source **factory boss** **no job** **front door** **factory**

b) Circle the term that describes the job of a **cell membrane**:

power source **factory boss** **no job** **front door** **factory**

c) Circle the term that describes the job of **cytoplasm**:

power source **factory boss** **no job** **front door** **factory**

Extension and Application

4. **You are the proud owner of a new cell factory!**

Pretend you have just bought a new factory. In this activity, the factory is a "cell factory". Use your imagination! You are the boss. This means you are in charge of everything that goes on inside the walls of your factory.

Choose ONE of the following:

Project A: Write a story describing how things run smoothly in your "cell factory".

Project B: Draw a detailed picture showing how things run smoothly in your "cell factory".

In your story or drawing, include the following information:

- If you are the boss, what part of the cell are you like? Describe its function.
- What other parts work together in your "cell team"?
  - cell membrane
  - cytoplasm
  - nucleus

5. **Practice your internet research skills!**

Storing food and carrying nutrients are two examples of specialized functions that cells have. **Pick ONE** of these jobs and create an information card presenting information you have found on the Internet.

Can you think of an interesting way to present your information? It could be a drawing, a game, a short story. Be creative! Make it interesting for the next person to read and learn about your cell function.

NAME: ______________________________

Cell Reproduction

1. Match the word on the left to its definition on the right. You may use a dictionary to help.

1	chromosome	A type of cell reproduction in which sex cells are produced	A
2	DNA	A small bit that holds a cell's genetic code	B
3	mitosis	Cell reproduction in which one cell divides into two, almost identical cells	C
4	meiosis	The process of cell reproduction in which sex cells are **not** produced	D
5	asexual reproduction	A long list of instructions that gives each cell in your body its own shape and function	E

2. Complete each sentence with a word from the list. You MAY use a dictionary for help.

mitosis **meiosis** **chromosome** **DNA**

a) In ____________________, sex cells are produced. A new individual is formed!

b) The secret code that made you at the start of your life is called your

____________________.

c) A ____________________ contains two copies of DNA, the secret code.

d) ____________________ is the process that creates a nearly exact copy of the original cell.

NAME: ______________________

Cell Reproduction

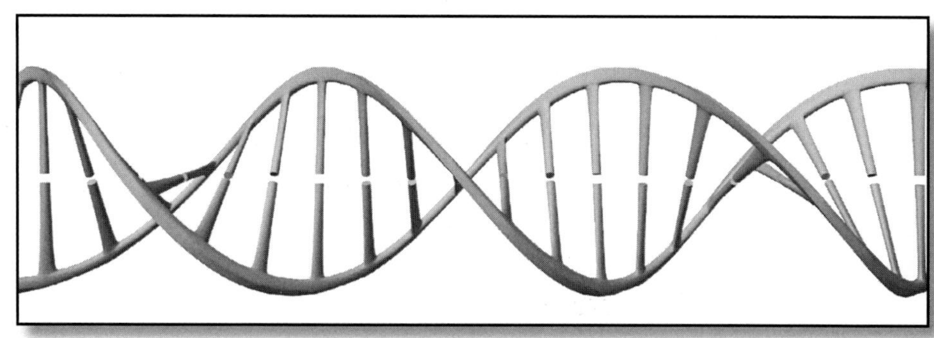

Remember how we found out that you began life as a single tiny cell? How do you think you grew from just one cell? That first cell had all the information and a list of instructions to make you the person you are now. These instructions were all written in a secret code in the middle of the cell. This code is called **DNA**. DNA is a very long list of instructions that gives each cell in your body its own shape and function.

STOP

If all humans started from one tiny cell, why do you think we all look and act differently?

____

____

____

That first cell grew a little and then small bits called **chromosomes** appeared. A **chromosome** contains two copies of DNA, the secret code to make you. Half of these chromosomes came from the egg cell. Half of them came from the sperm cell. That first cell then divided into two separate cells by a process called **mitosis**. In mitosis, a nearly exact copy of the original cell is formed. We classify this as **asexual reproduction** because one cell divides into two new, almost identical cells. **Meiosis** is the other type of cell reproduction. In this process, cells also duplicate their contents and then divide to produce two cells. In meiosis however, **sex cells** are produced. There are two different sex cells: sperm cells and egg cells. Males produce sperm cells and females produce egg cells. Meiosis is classified as **sexual reproduction**. In meiosis, a sperm cell fertilizes an egg cell. These two cells unite and create a new individual cell.

Mitosis and **meiosis** are similar processes because new cells are formed from cells that already exist. They are different, however, in the way new cells are created.
Cell reproduction for all plants and animals falls into one of these two categories.

NAME: ___________________________

Cell Reproduction

1. Put a check mark (✓) next to the answer that is most correct.

a) How do you think you grew from just one cell?

- ◯ **A** Humans don't grow from just one cell. They start with many cells.
- ◯ **B** That one cell grew in size and therefore you grew taller.
- ◯ **C** That first cell had all the information and a list of instructions to make you the person you are now.
- ◯ **D** That one cell used oxygen from the lungs to expand in size.

b) What very important job does <u>DNA</u> have?

- ◯ **A** It helps cells move around using "paddles".
- ◯ **B** It gives instructions to the cells in your body.
- ◯ **C** It keeps the cell protected from other things that are trying to get in.
- ◯ **D** It acts as a "power source", just like cytoplasm.

c) What categories does all cell reproduction fall into?

- ◯ **A** sperm and egg
- ◯ **B** nucleus and cytoplasm
- ◯ **C** meiosis and mitosis
- ◯ **D** labor and delivery

d) In mitosis, where do chromosomes come from?

- ◯ **A** They come from the nucleus in the cell.
- ◯ **B** They are not part of any reproduction process.
- ◯ **C** They come only from sperm cells.
- ◯ **D** Half of the chromosomes come from the sperm cell, half of them come from the egg cell.

e) How is <u>meiosis</u> different from <u>mitosis</u>?

- ◯ **A** In meiosis, sex cells are produced. They are not produced in mitosis.
- ◯ **B** They are the same thing but the author just spelled them incorrectly.
- ◯ **C** Meiosis is a cell reproduction process and mitosis is not.
- ◯ **D** In meiosis, the cell's contents duplicate. In mitosis, they do not.

NAME: ______________________

Cell Reproduction

2. Use a dictionary to look up the definitions of MITOSIS and MEIOSIS. Write down the dictionary's definition, and then write your own definition of each word.

a) mitosis (dictionary): ______________________

b) mitosis (own definition): ______________________

c) meiosis (dictionary): ______________________

d) meiosis (own definition): ______________________

Extension and Application

3. Write your own secret code – DNA!

Remember, DNA is a very long list of instructions that gives each cell in your body its own shape and function. Your DNA's instructions made you the person you are now.

Put yourself in the shoes of DNA. Be creative, and come up with a **list of instructions** that you feel have made you who you are now. Be sure to use scientific terms from the reading passage in your answer, showing that you understand the processes of cell reproduction.

Write your answer in a list, almost like a To Do list. Label each instruction as: 1… 2… 3… 4… Try to come up with at least **eight** instructions!

4. You are the teacher!

Pretend you are teaching your class a lesson on **cell reproduction**. Your teacher probably uses a chalkboard to write notes, draw pictures and explain things. Use the "chalkboard" on the next page to give a lesson on cell reproduction. Most importantly, explain both **mitosis** and **meiosis**. Use words, pictures, and arrows!

By the end of this activity, show a classmate your answer. Ask them, "**Do you understand what cell reproduction means by looking at my chalkboard?**" They should answer yes. If they are unclear, go back and add more information to make your lesson clearer.

Have fun being the teacher!

NAME: ______________________________

Cell Reproduction

NAME: ______________________

Plant and Animal Cells

1. In the first box below, draw a picture of a PLANT that you have taken care of in the past. This could be a plant in your classroom or at home. In the second box, draw what you think a PLANT CELL might look like. Use your imagination! There is no right answer for this question.

PLANT	PLANT CELL

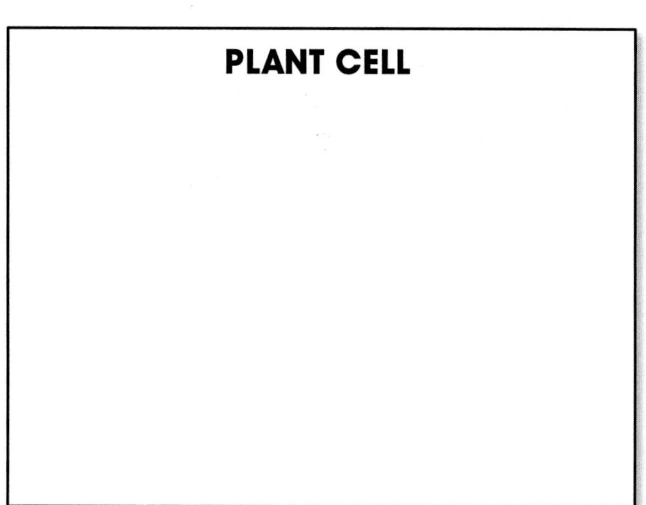

2. Complete each sentence with a term from the list. Use a dictionary to help you.

cell wall **vacuole** **plastid** **centriole** **lysosome**

a) A ____________________ is a round organelle in an animal cell. In it are digestive enzymes.

b) The outside covering of a plant cell is called the ____________________.

c) A ____________________ is a compartment in a plant cell. It is surrounded by a membrane and is filled with fluid.

d) A structure in an animal cell that lies very close to the center of the nucleus is called a ____________________.

e) A specialized structure in a plant cell that stores food is called a ____________________.

NAME: ______________________________

Plant and Animal Cells

We have read that there are many different types of cells. Let's look at the cells that make up plants and those that make up animals. **Plant cells** and **animal cells** have similar parts, or structures. For example, both have a nucleus and cell membrane. They also make up single-celled and multicellular organisms. Animal cells, however, are more specialized than plant cells. They take on special functions within tissues that plant cells do not.

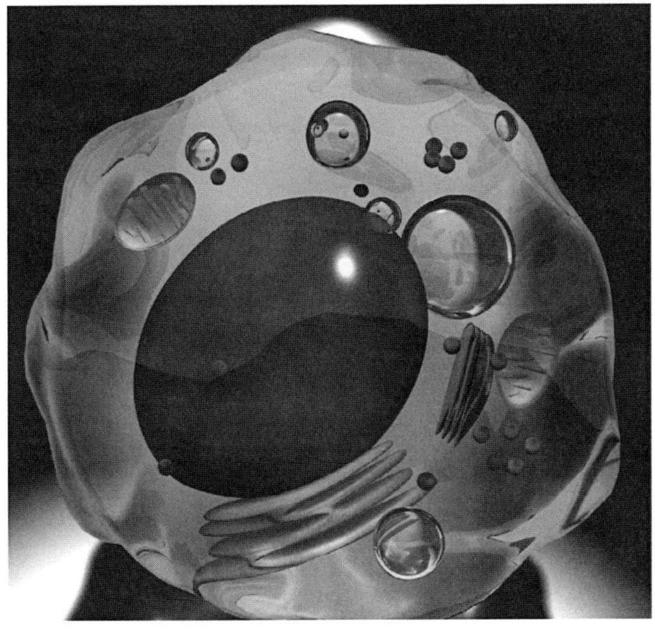

Plant cells have three structures that do not exist in animal cells: cell walls, vacuoles, and plastids. The **cell wall** is the rigid outer covering of the cell. It is an extra layer that surrounds even the cell membrane, forming a double barricade! Plant cells also have **vacuoles**. These are large sacs in a cell that take up a lot of space. Vacuoles are also covered by a membrane. Their job is to be a storage space for proteins, waste and other cell products. Plant cells also have **plastids**, structures in the cell that make or store food.

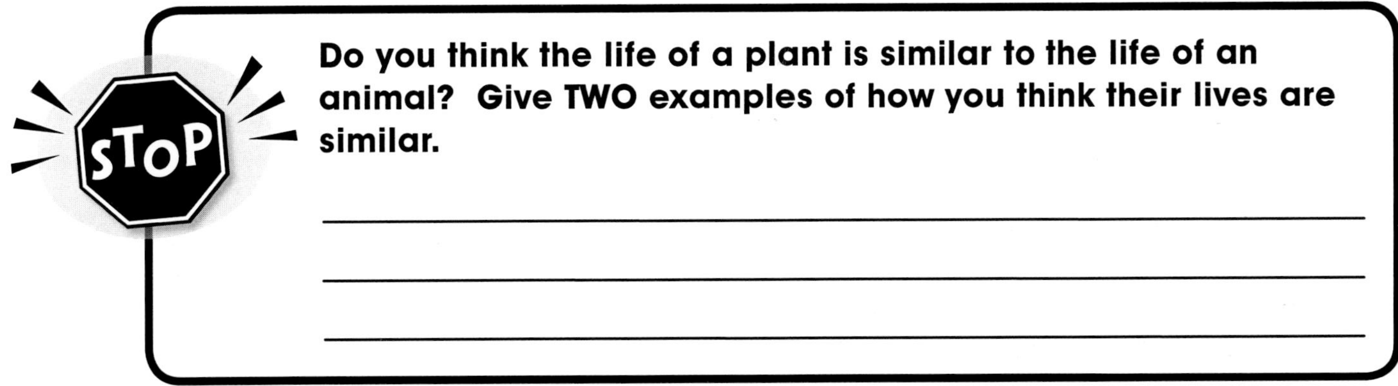

Do you think the life of a plant is similar to the life of an animal? Give TWO examples of how you think their lives are similar.

____

____

____

Animal cells have two structures that are not found in plant cells. A **centriole** is the thick, dense center of the "organizing center" of an animal cell. A **lysosome** is a round organelle that contains digestive enzymes. Cell nutrients are digested in the lysosome. Plant and animal cells differ because of these unique structures that are found in each of them.

NAME: ______________________

Plant and Animal Cells

1. (Circle) the word True if the statement is true. (Circle) the word False if it's false.

a) Single-celled and multicellular organisms can be made of plant cells or animal cells.

True **False**

b) Plant cells are more specialized than animal cells.

True **False**

c) Plant cells have only one structure that does not exist in animal cells: a cell wall.

True **False**

d) Plastids are structures in plant cells whose job is to store or make food.

True **False**

e) Animal cells have two structures that are not found in plant cells: a centriole and a lysosome.

True **False**

2. Write each word besides its meaning. There is ONE word that does NOT have a matching definition! Use the reading passage to write a definition for the remaining word.

plastid **cell wall** **centriole** **lysosome** **vacuole**

[ ] **a)** The dense center of the "organizing center" of an animal cell

[ ] **b)** A large membrane-bound sac that takes up a large amount of space in a plant cell

[ ] **c)** A structure in a plant cell that makes or stores food

[ ] **d)** The rigid outer covering of a plant cell

[ ] **e)** ______________________

NAME: ____________________

After You Read

Plant and Animal Cells

Answer the questions in complete sentences.

3. How are animal cells more **specialized** than plant cells?

____

4. What **three** structures do plants cells have that animal cells do not? Name and describe them.

____

5. What **two** structures do animal cells have that plant cells do not? Name and describe them.

____

Extension and Application

6. A Contest: Plant Cells versus Animal Cells!

Copy the following chart into your notes. Use facts from both the reading passage and other research tools to fill in the chart. This chart is just a guideline. Use as much space as you need to answer or fill in each section.

Once you have written facts in your notes, ask your teacher for a large sheet of paper. **Transfer your notes** neatly onto this large sheet of paper. Hang it up in the classroom and share your information with the rest of the class.

Plant Cells	**Animal Cells**
A picture of what a plant cell looks like... like...	A picture of what an animal cell looks
A plant cell's special structures are...	An animal cell's special structures are...
The function of each special structure is...	The function of each special structure is...

Before You Read

NAME: ____________________

From Cells to Organisms

1. Draw a line from the word on the left to its matching definition. Which word is left over? Use the reading passage or a dictionary to help you write out its definition.

1	**tissue**	A group of tissues in a plant or animal that have a specific function	A
2	**organ system**	The smallest unit of life that all living things are made of	B
3	**organism**	Any living thing such as a plant, animal or bacteria	C
4	**organ**	A group of cells that all have a similar job to do	D
5	**cell**	____________________ ____________________	E

2. Look at the matched definitions in the question above. Use each vocabulary word in your own sentence. Make sure your sentence shows that you understand what the word means.

a) organ ____________________

____

b) tissue ____________________

____

c) organism ____________________

____

d) cell ____________________

____

NAME: ____________________

From Cells to Organisms

We have read that cells are the building blocks of life. They are the smallest unit of life, and all living things are made of cells. But how do a bunch of cells make up a whole multicellular organism, like a lizard, a bear or a human? Let's look at how multicellular organisms are **organized**, from the smallest unit (cells), to the biggest unit (organisms).

Cells
Tissues
Organs
Organ Systems
Organism

Similar cells group together to make **tissue**. So, tissue is a group of cells that have a special job to do, or a specific function. In many animals, there are four main types of tissue: epithelial tissue, connective tissue, muscle tissue and nerve tissue. Each kind of tissue has its own job to do. For example, muscle tissue is made of muscle cells that let an animal's body move. Connective tissue is made of cells that are strong and attach one bone to the next.

STOP

Can you think of at least FIVE organs in the human body?

____

____

____

Organs are made of different kinds of tissues that work together. Animals have many different organs in their bodies. You have likely heard of the following: the liver, kidneys, and the heart. Did you know that even your skin is an organ? It is the largest organ in your body!

Different organs work together to perform a specific function in the body. A group of organs is called an **organ system**. Lizard, bears, humans and other animals have many organ systems. Three examples are the digestive system, skeletal system and nervous system. Each of these systems has a very important job to do; they carry out the processes of life. And finally, all of an animal's organ systems work together and form the biggest unit of life – the **organism**.

After You Read

NAME: ______________________

From Cells to Organisms

1. Circle the word True if the statement is true. Circle the word False if it's false.

a) An organ is the smallest unit of life. It is able to carry out all the functions of living things.

True **False**

b) Water, blood and oxygen are three main tissue types in the human body.

True **False**

c) Your skin is the largest organ in your body.

True **False**

d) Connective tissue is made of strong muscle cells.

True **False**

e) Cells group together in the following way to form multicellular organisms:

cells → tissues → organs → organ systems → organism

True **False**

2. Circle the answer that best completes each sentence.

a) A(n) ______________ is a group of cells that perform a specific function.

organ **tissue**

b) An ______________ is made of organ systems which carry out the processes of life.

organism **organ**

c) The heart, liver and kidneys are all examples of ______________ in the human body.

organs **cells**

d) ______________ tissue allows your body to move.

connective **muscle**

NAME: ______________________

From Cells to Organisms

Answer the questions in complete sentences.

3. What is an **organ**? Give an example of an organ in the human body.

____

4. What is the difference between an **organ** and an **organ system**? Use an example to explain your answer.

____

5. What role does the **muscle tissue** have in an animal's body?

____

Extension and Application

6. Did you know?

In this activity, you will prepare a Did You Know? **fact sheet** on the largest organ in your body – the **skin**! Use various research tools (books, Internet, etc.) to find facts and information about the skin. For example, what job does it have?

On a large piece of Bristol board, prepare your list of facts. Write down the facts that you find most interesting. How can you organize and present your facts in a creative way? Use your imagination!

7. Create an organ team!

Working in groups of **four**, you will form an "organ team". You will each be science researchers for this activity. Each group member will choose a different organ from the following list:

lungs **heart** **brain** **kidney** **stomach** **liver**

You will work **independently** to research your chosen organ. Once you have found enough information on your chosen organ, transfer your information onto Bristol board. Your Bristol board should not be in its regular square format. Cut it out in the shape of the organ you are researching.

You will then come together as an organ team and present your information to the rest of the class. Good luck with the research!

NAME: ______________________

Diffusion and Osmosis

1. In the squares below, draw pictures of things that you think HUMANS need to stay alive. Write your answers on the line in the square.

2. In the squares below, draw pictures of things that you think PLANTS need to stay alive. Write your answers on the line in the square.

3. Complete each sentence with a word from the list. Use a dictionary to help you.

osmosis **diffusion** **permeable**

a) ____________________ is the process in which something spreads throughout something else.

b) Something is ____________________ if it allows liquids or gases to pass through.

c) In ____________________, molecules pass through a semi-permeable membrane until there are equal amounts of the molecules on both sides of the membrane.

NAME: ____________________

Diffusion and Osmosis

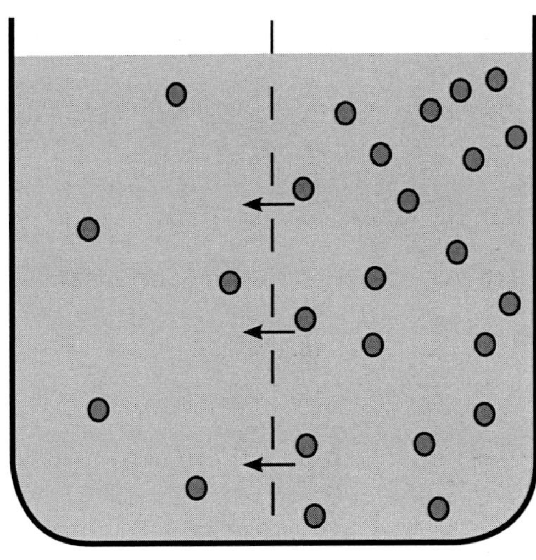
(Motion of Diffusion)

How do humans stay alive? We need to eat, drink, breathe, sleep, etc. All plants and animals have things they must do to stay alive. Also, all plant and animal cells must do certain things to stay alive. In order for a cell to live, tiny bits of matter, called **particles**, move into and out of the cell. They get in and out by passing through the **cell membrane**, the cell's outside "wall".

Particles can pass through a cell membrane in two ways: by active transport and passive transport. In **active transport**, energy from food is needed to move the particles across the cell membrane. **Passive transport** happens randomly. It does not need energy from food to help move the particles.

Describe what you think is the difference between someone who is ACTIVE and someone who is PASSIVE.

____

____

Imagine you are standing in a room of 100 people but you don't like crowded places. The room next door has only two people in it. What would you do? You would move to the room with fewer people! When this happens in cells, it is called **diffusion**. In diffusion, particles move from an area where there are many other particles to an area where there are fewer particles. Diffusion is a form of passive transport. It can occur across a cell membrane. The membrane allows small particles like water and oxygen to move into or out of the cell.

What happens if a molecule is too large to pass through a cell membrane? Then it moves by **osmosis**, a special type of diffusion. The molecule can move into or out of the cell because the cell has a **semi-permeable membrane**. This means that the cell lets some molecules pass through and not others. Osmosis is a form of passive transport that helps keep the cell alive.

After You Read

NAME: ____________________

Diffusion and Osmosis

1. Circle the word True if the statement is true. Circle the word False if it's false.

a) All living things have certain things they need to do to stay alive.

True **False**

b) Particles move into and out of cells by passing through the nucleus.

True **False**

c) Particles can move through the membrane in two ways: by **active transport** and by **passive transport**.

True **False**

d) **Passive transport** needs energy from food to move the particles. **Active transport** does not.

True **False**

e) A **semi-permeable membrane** allows only some particles to pass through it.

True **False**

2. Write each word besides its meaning. There is ONE word that does NOT have a matching definition! Use the reading passage to write a definition for the remaining word.

diffusion **osmosis** **active transport** **semi-permeable**

______ **a)** Describes something that allows some things through it, and not others

______ **b)** The movement of particles from an area with lots of other particles to an area where there are fewer particles

______ **c)** One way in which particles move back and forth across a membrane. It uses energy from food to move the particles.

______ **d)** ____________________

NAME: ______________________

Diffusion and Osmosis

3. Use a dictionary to look up the definition of OSMOSIS and DIFFUSION. Write down the dictionary's definitions. Then write a sentence using each word that shows the meaning of the word.

a) osmosis (dictionary): ______________________

b) osmosis (own definition): ______________________

c) diffusion (dictionary): ______________________

d) diffusion (own definition): ______________________

Extension and Application

4. A Semi-permeable Experiment!

For this activity, you will be working with a partner. You are both scientists doing an experiment to figure out which materials are **semi-permeable**. Remember what semi-permeable means: it describes something that allows some things to pass through it and not others. You will experiment with water to discover which materials it can pass through.

Test the following materials to find out if they are **semi-permeable**:

- paper towel
- sheet of paper
- T-shirt
- plastic wrap
- towel
- any other materials you can think of (Use your imagination!)

You will be testing these materials out over a sink. Using a cup of water, pour the water over the material. Does water pass through the material? Record your observations in your notebook.

5. Be a Textbook Illustrator!

Pretend you are the illustrator who draws pictures for your science textbook. You are working on the chapter about **osmosis**. Using information from the reading passage and other research tools, draw a picture that describes **osmosis**. Include the following features in your drawing: a container, water, large particles, small particles and a semi-permeable membrane. Remember to label your drawing. Use a pencil for your drawing!

Brush Up on Your Microscope Skills!

CELLS are the building blocks of life.
They are the smallest unit of living matter. Even if you tried very hard, you would not be able to see a single cell with just your eyes.
That's what a MICROSCOPE is for.

In this activity, you will take a few minutes to collect **four living things** from your surroundings. Remember: they have to be living! Here are some suggestions on where to look:

- **Your school yard (in the soil, plants, bugs)**
- **A plant in your classroom**
- **Anything that is growing (including you!)**

Using a microscope, you will **investigate** what the cells in your four living things look like. While you are using the microscope, think about the following questions:

- **What SHAPE is the cell?**
- **What SIZE is the cell compared to other cells you have seen?**
- **Are there any other FEATURES that are unique to this cell?**

Make a chart like the one below to record your observations. Enlarge the chart in your notes – you will need more room for your pictures and words than the small squares below!

	DIAGRAM of what you see	DESCRIPTION of what you see
Living Thing #1		
Living Thing #2		
Living Thing #3		
Living Thing #4		

Sculpt a Plasticine Cell!

We have learned that even though all cells are different, they have some parts in common. There are three parts that all cells have in common.

Do you remember what they are?

CLUES...

1. The outside covering that holds all parts of the cell in place is called... **a cell membrane**.
2. The dark part located in the middle of the cell (the "brain" of the cell) is called... a **nucleus**.
3. The jelly-like substance that fills in the inside of a cell, where all the cell's activities take place is called... **cytoplasm**.

FOR THIS ACTIVITY, you will need:

- 3 different colors of plasticine
- 3 toothpicks
- small pieces of paper
- tape

STEPS:

1. Use plasticine to **sculpt** what you think a cell would look like based on the three cell parts described above. Use a different **color** for each cell part. The cell should be **at least** the size of your hand.
2. Once you have finished sculpting your cell, place the toothpicks in the plasticine. You will use them as markers for the different cell parts.
3. On a small piece of paper, write down the cell part. "Flag" it by sticking the toothpick in the pasticine.
4. Tape the label (small piece of paper) to the toothpick.

When you are finished, someone should be able to look at your plasticine cell and see the three different parts labeled. Have fun sculpting!

Design a DNA Instruction Book

BUILD A PERSON!

DNA is a secret code found in the middle of the cell, in the NUCLEUS. It is a very long list of instructions that gives each cell in your body its own shape and function. Your DNA made you the person you are now!

Now it is your turn to pretend you are the DNA. You will design your own person by creating your own list of instructions. Use your imagination for this activity! You can design any person you can imagine!!

DESIGN AN INSTRUCTION BOOKLET:

Think about something you recently bought at a store that needs instructions to assemble it. It likely came with a small foldout book that shows (with big numbers!) how to assemble the object, giving detailed instructions for each step.

Your teacher will bring in a few examples of such books in case you have never seen one before. Use it as a guideline for your own book you will design.

YOUR BOOK SHOULD INCLUDE:

- A cover page (just like a title page – use diagrams and words to introduce your book)
- Numbers to show each step
- Creative instructions on how to build a person

Use **pictures** as well as words! It should be easy to follow and fun to look at!

Use the following page format for your instruction book:

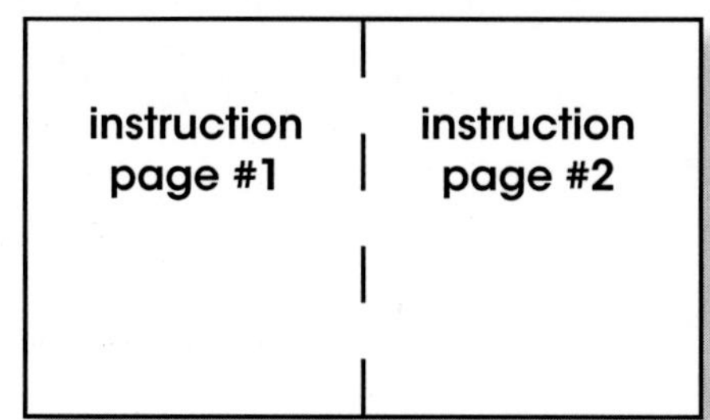

Watercolor Plant and Animal Cells!

We have learned that plant cells and animal cells have some important differences. They have different parts, or structures.

To review, here are the differences...

PLANT CELLS have three structures that do not exist in animal cells:

- **Cells walls** (outer covering)
- **Vacuoles** (large membrane-bound sac that takes up a large amount of space)
- **Plastids** (structures in the cell that make or store food)

ANIMAL CELLS have two structures that do not exist in plant cells:

- **Centrioles** (dense center of the "organizing center" of the cell)
- **Lyosome** (round organelle that contains digestive enzymes)

ACTIVITY:

In this activity, you will use watercolors to paint what animal and plant cells look like. Before you start painting, cut one large piece of white craft paper. Draw a line down the middle of the paper like you see in the diagram below. Use a pencil to sketch out the outlines of your drawings. Once you have completed your sketches, you are ready to start painting!

Remember to label your drawing with all the cell parts mentioned above!

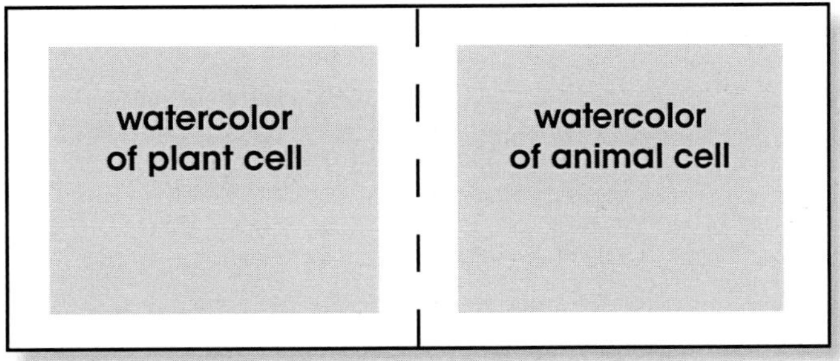

After You Read

NAME: ____________________

Crossword Puzzle!

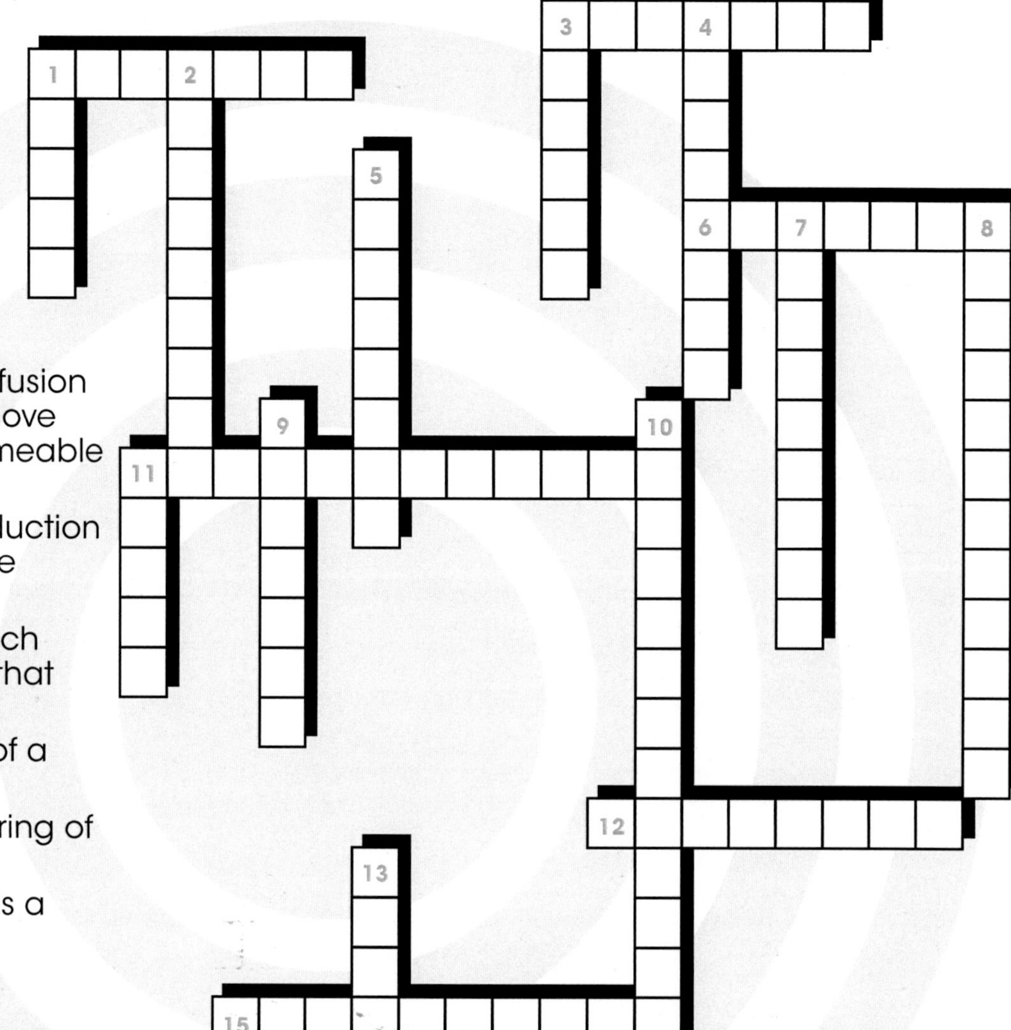

Across

1 A special type of diffusion in which particles move through a semi-permeable membrane

3 A type of cell reproduction in which sex cells are produced

6 The cell's "brain" which controls everything that happens in the cell

11 The outer covering of a cell

12 The rigid outer covering of a plant cell

15 A small bit that holds a cell's genetic code

Down

1 Something that is made of different kinds of tissue working together

2 A small structure found inside a cell

3 Anything that has mass and takes up space

4 A living thing, such as a plant or animal

5 Large sacs in a plant cell that take up a lot of space

7 Jelly-like substance that fills the inside of a cell

8 Describes an organism that is made up of only one tiny cell

9 Structure in a plant cell that makes or stores food

10 Describes something that allows some things through it, and not others

11 "Paddles" that push the cells around and make them move

13 Type of cell reproduction in which one cell divides into two new, almost identical cells

NAME: ________________________________

Word Search

Find all of the words in the Word Search. Words may be horizontal, vertical, or diagonal. A few may even be backwards! Look carefully!

matter	centriole	multicellular	organelle
cell	lysosome	single-celled	cilia
magnify	tissue	nucleus	chromosome
microscope	organ	DNA	mitosis
organism	diffusion	membrane	meiosis
specialization	osmosis	particle	vacuole
amoeba	semi-permeable	cytoplasm	plastid

e	s	i	n	g	l	e	c	e	l	l	e	d	b	n	m	j	n
f	p	j	h	d	h	y	h	f	d	o	r	g	a	n	i	s	m
g	e	w	r	f	c	e	r	g	v	q	h	p	o	t	u	e	u
j	c	j	g	e	q	g	o	h	a	w	g	u	p	l	m	k	l
t	i	s	s	u	e	f	m	j	c	e	f	y	a	b	e	j	t
k	a	m	o	e	b	a	o	m	u	r	d	t	r	t	i	h	i
l	l	r	h	v	x	b	s	n	o	t	s	a	t	a	o	g	c
p	i	n	l	k	t	v	o	b	l	y	n	r	i	h	s	f	e
o	z	e	u	r	d	c	m	v	e	e	e	l	c	l	i	d	l
e	a	o	x	c	q	i	e	r	t	y	i	w	l	y	s	s	l
p	t	s	c	y	l	f	f	g	h	c	y	l	e	t	e	x	u
o	i	m	v	t	w	e	b	f	l	k	r	e	t	t	a	m	l
c	o	o	b	o	e	e	u	s	u	j	h	g	f	d	s	a	a
s	n	s	j	p	r	r	r	s	l	s	k	j	h	g	f	d	r
o	n	i	m	l	t	f	t	h	u	s	i	l	m	n	b	v	e
r	b	s	n	a	y	v	y	h	j	j	o	o	v	f	d	s	l
c	g	t	b	s	p	l	a	s	t	i	d	l	n	f	d	d	o
i	n	t	h	m	u	x	x	c	v	b	n	m	e	k	j	n	i
m	a	g	n	i	f	y	z	s	i	s	o	t	i	m	h	a	r
t	g	c	s	e	m	i	p	e	r	m	e	a	b	l	e	m	t
h	r	e	d	o	l	b	n	m	v	c	w	e	r	t	y	u	n
g	o	l	y	s	o	s	o	m	e	s	r	e	t	t	a	m	e
f	v	l	d	e	l	l	e	n	a	g	r	o	n	k	j	l	c

After You Read

NAME: ____________________

Comprehension Quiz

Part A

Circle the word True if the statement is true. Circle the word False if it is false.

1. Most organisms are made up of millions of cells. There are also some organisms that are made up one cell

   True **False**

2. A cactus, a human and an oak tree are all examples of single-celled organisms.

   True **False**

3. The cell's nucleus is like a front door. It controls everything that passes in and out of the cell.

   True **False**

4. Most organisms are made up of many specialized cells which carry out specific functions that support the life of the organism.

   True **False**

5. Meiosis and mitosis are two types of cell reproduction.

   True **False**

6. Plant cells can only be found in single-celled organisms. Animal cells can only be found in multicellular organisms.

   True **False**

Part B

On the diagram below, label the three main parts of a cell. Use the words in the list.

nucleus **cell membrane** **cytoplasm**

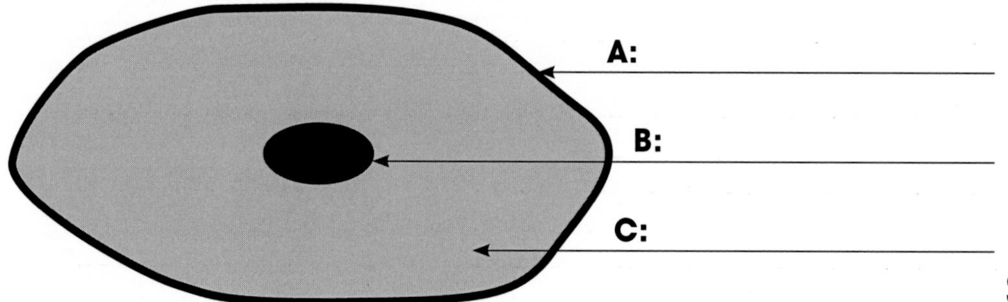

SUBTOTAL: /9

NAME: ______________________________

Comprehension Quiz

Part C

Answer the questions in complete sentences.

1. What is a **cell**? What would you need to use in order to see a cell? 3

____

____

____

2. What function does a cell's **DNA** have? Where in the cell is **DNA** found? 3

____

____

3. Name **two parts of a cell**. Describe their **function** in the cell. 4

____

____

____

4. Is there a difference between **meiosis** and **mitosis**? Explain. 3

____

____

5. Describe two structures that **plant cells have** that **animal cells do not have**. 3

____

____

____

____

SUBTOTAL: /16

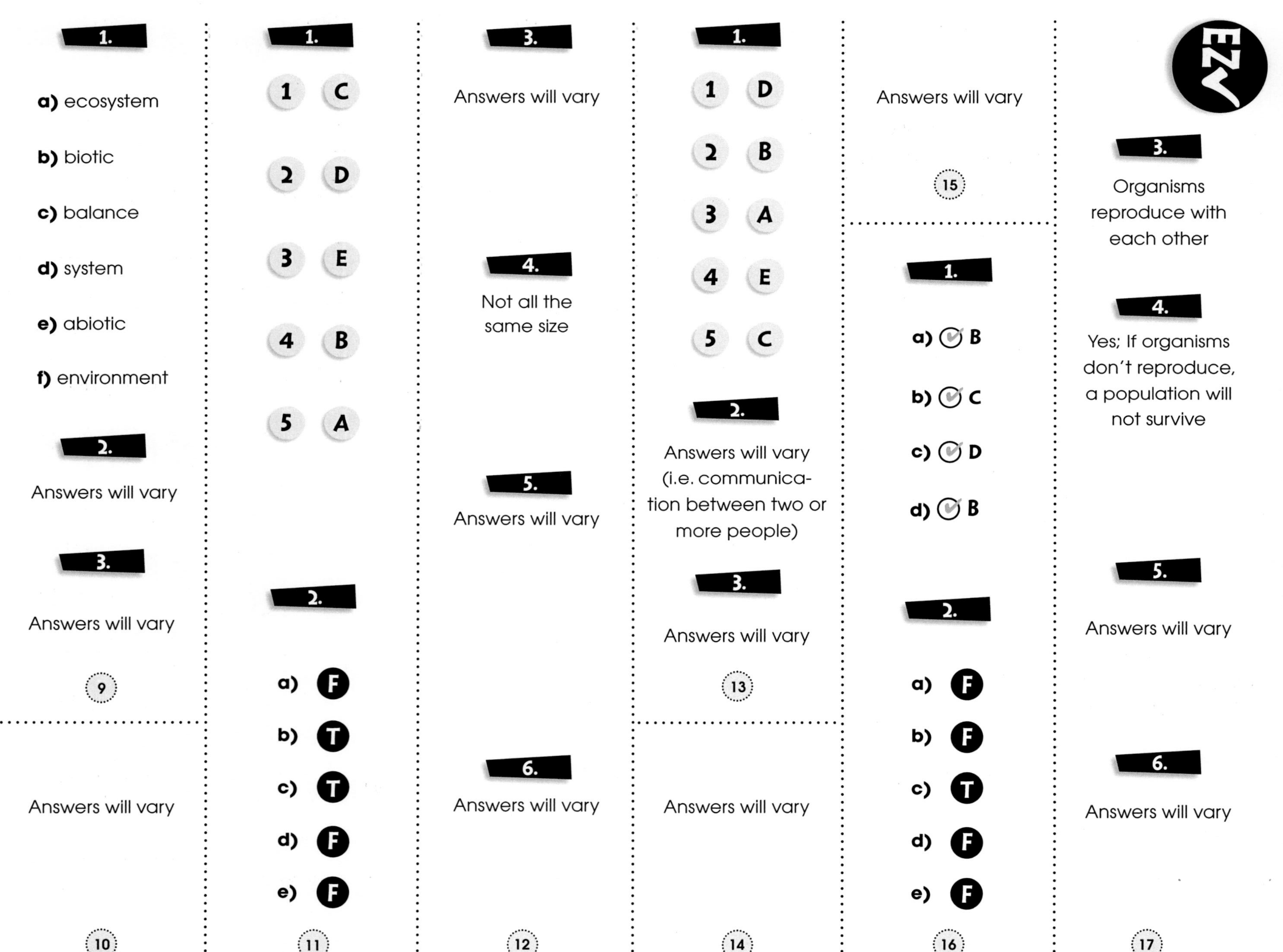

EZ✓

Page 9

1.

a) ecosystem

b) biotic

c) balance

d) system

e) abiotic

f) environment

2. Answers will vary

3. Answers will vary

Page 10

Answers will vary

Page 11

1.

1 C

2 D

3 E

4 B

5 A

2.

a) F

b) T

c) T

d) F

e) F

Page 12

3. Answers will vary

4. Not all the same size

5. Answers will vary

6. Answers will vary

Page 13

1.

1 D

2 B

3 A

4 E

5 C

2. Answers will vary (i.e. communication between two or more people)

3. Answers will vary

Page 14

Answers will vary

Page 15

Answers will vary

Page 16

1.

a) ✓ B

b) ✓ C

c) ✓ D

d) ✓ B

2.

a) F

b) F

c) T

d) F

e) F

Page 17

3. Organisms reproduce with each other

4. Yes; If organisms don't reproduce, a population will not survive

5. Answers will vary

6. Answers will vary

1.

a) Answers will vary

b) Answers will vary

2.

a) succession

b) ecosystem

c) biotic

d) environment

e) composition

f) population

18

Answers will vary

19

1.

a) every

b) ecosystems

c) composition

d) change

e) humans

2.

a) F

b) T

c) F

d) T

e) T

20

3.

All parts of an ecosystem

4.

Population may grow, shrink, or disappear; species might move into ecosystem

5.

Answers will vary (i.e. cut down trees, develop land for houses)

6.

Answers will vary

21

1.

Answers will vary

2.

a) sun

b) decomposer

c) recycle

d) producer

e) consumer

23

Answers will vary

24

1.

producer – **E**

decomposer – **C**

consumer – **D**

recycle – **A**

the sun – **B**

2.

Into 3 categories: producers, consumers, decomposers

3.

Producers make their own food, consumers depend on others for food

25

4.

Breaks down materials in dead organisms

5.

They all depend on each other for food and energy

6.

Answers will vary

26

EZ✓

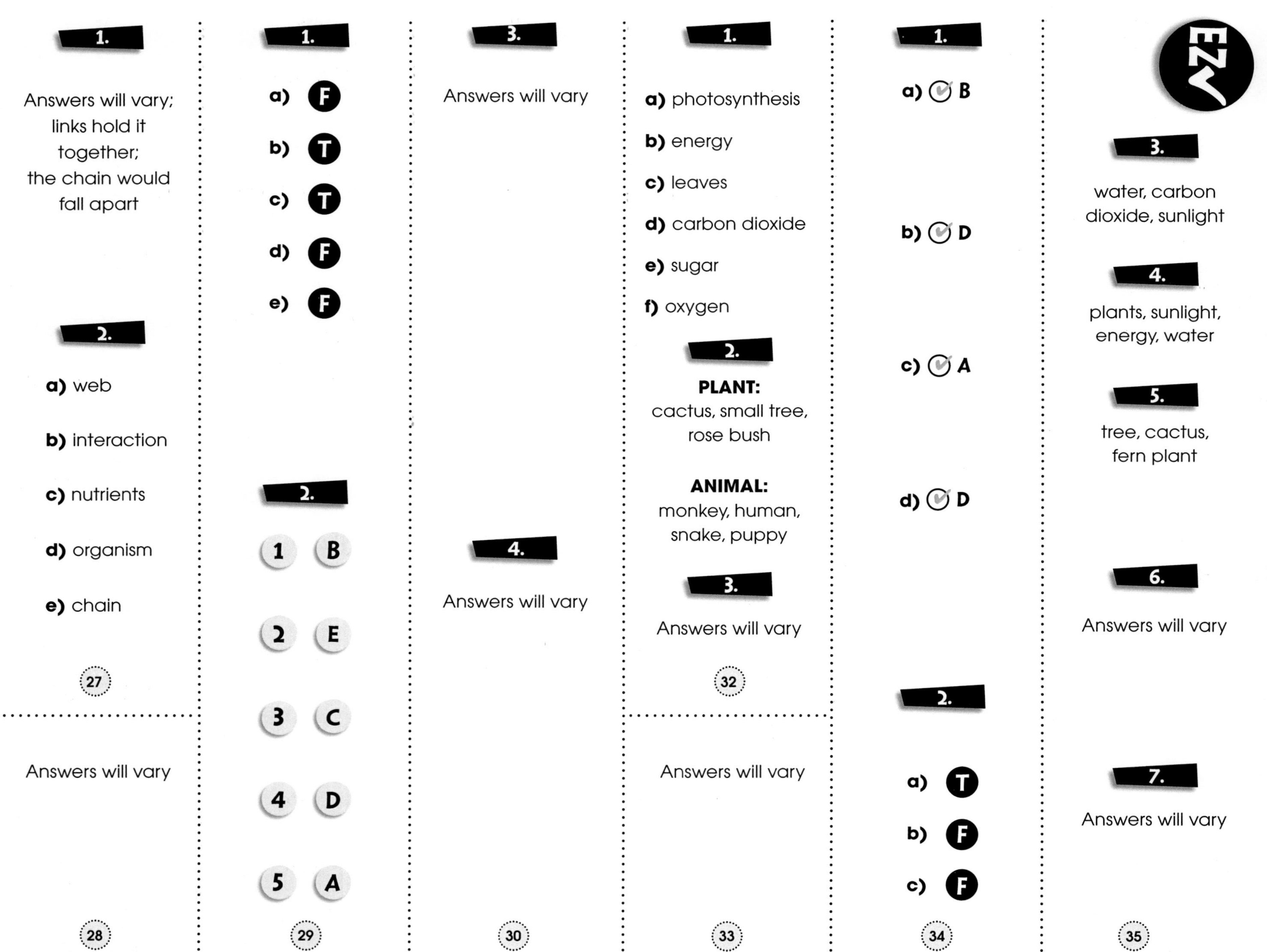

Page 27

1. Answers will vary; links hold it together; the chain would fall apart

2.
- **a)** web
- **b)** interaction
- **c)** nutrients
- **d)** organism
- **e)** chain

Page 28

Answers will vary

Page 29

1.
- a) F
- b) T
- c) T
- d) F
- e) F

2.
- 1 B
- 2 E
- 3 C
- 4 D
- 5 A

Page 30

3. Answers will vary

4. Answers will vary

Page 32

1.
- **a)** photosynthesis
- **b)** energy
- **c)** leaves
- **d)** carbon dioxide
- **e)** sugar
- **f)** oxygen

2.
PLANT: cactus, small tree, rose bush

ANIMAL: monkey, human, snake, puppy

3. Answers will vary

Page 33

Answers will vary

Page 34

1.
- a) ✓ B
- b) ✓ D
- c) ✓ A
- d) ✓ D

2.
- a) T
- b) F
- c) F

Page 35

EZ✓

3. water, carbon dioxide, sunlight

4. plants, sunlight, energy, water

5. tree, cactus, fern plant

6. Answers will vary

7. Answers will vary

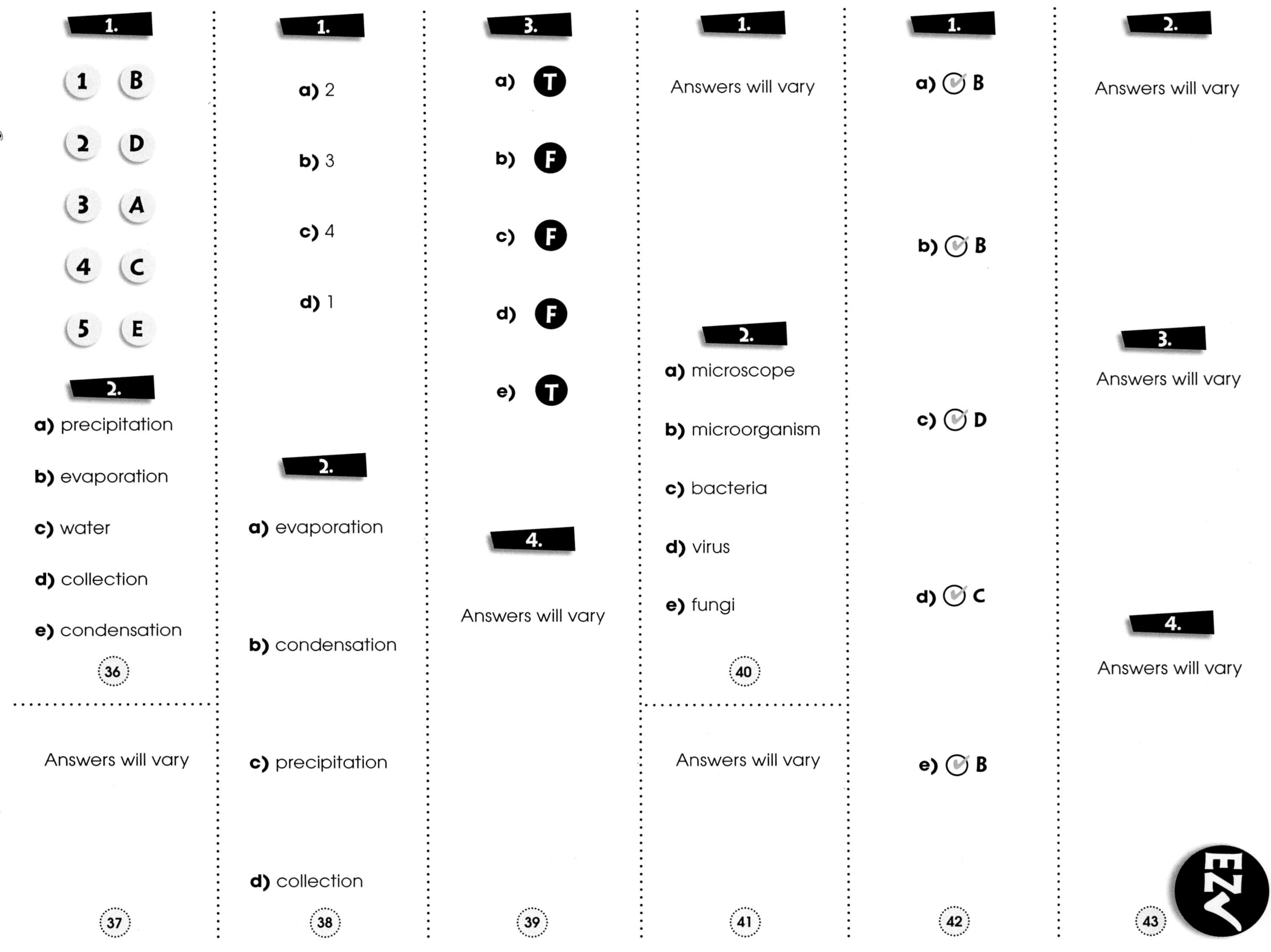

1.

1 B

2 D

3 A

4 C

5 E

2.

a) precipitation

b) evaporation

c) water

d) collection

e) condensation

36

Answers will vary

37

1.

a) 2

b) 3

c) 4

d) 1

2.

a) evaporation

b) condensation

c) precipitation

d) collection

38

3.

a) T

b) F

c) F

d) F

e) T

4.

Answers will vary

39

1.

Answers will vary

2.

a) microscope

b) microorganism

c) bacteria

d) virus

e) fungi

40

Answers will vary

41

1.

a) B

b) B

c) D

d) C

e) B

42

2.

Answers will vary

3.

Answers will vary

4.

Answers will vary

43

Across:

1. ecosystem

4. abiotic

5. bacteria

7. recycle

8. microscope

10. condensation

13. microorganism

Down:

1. energy

2. sugar

3. evaporation

5. biotic

6. consumer

8. water cycle

9. collection

11. population

12. decomposer

14. virus

Word Search Answers

b	a	c	t	e	r	i	a	v	e	e	c	n	a	l	a	b	n
w	o	d	r	e	c	y	c	l	e	r	t	h	t	n	v	b	u
e	e	r	c	o	n	d	e	n	s	a	t	i	o	n	z	c	s
n	t	z	g	w	e	f	g	t	y	x	b	q	e	r	z	o	t
v	n	c	w	a	r	n	u	t	r	i	e	n	t	s	q	n	s
i	o	v	s	q	n	w	e	c	o	s	y	s	t	e	m	s	h
r	i	b	d	w	e	i	j	w	w	r	w	j	h	s	a	u	e
o	t	b	f	y	n	f	s	r	e	d	b	k	g	d	p	m	e
n	a	n	g	u	b	g	h	m	d	c	v	f	f	e	h	e	h
m	r	y	g	r	e	n	e	t	w	w	a	b	d	c	o	r	e
e	o	g	h	g	v	h	r	y	k	e	r	g	s	o	t	n	e
n	p	h	r	n	o	i	t	a	l	u	p	o	p	m	o	l	y
t	a	p	j	e	c	y	b	y	n	g	d	x	w	p	s	r	k
v	v	j	r	h	p	j	v	c	g	d	h	y	e	o	y	y	s
r	e	k	k	o	q	r	c	u	i	n	m	g	r	s	n	e	u
e	t	y	v	j	d	u	o	o	w	t	b	e	t	e	t	d	c
b	b	i	i	k	t	u	x	d	d	s	o	n	y	r	h	s	c
n	i	g	r	b	r	k	c	e	u	w	h	i	h	m	e	c	e
m	o	n	u	e	e	r	w	e	d	c	a	v	b	n	s	n	s
r	t	u	s	w	q	w	e	r	r	y	e	d	f	a	i	v	s
y	i	f	o	o	d	c	h	a	i	n	h	g	j	k	s	v	i
k	c	c	c	o	m	p	o	s	i	t	i	o	n	r	y	e	o
g	q	e	m	s	i	n	a	g	r	o	o	r	c	i	m	s	n

Part A

1. T
2. F
3. T
4. T
5. F
6. T
7. F
8. F

Part B

1.

A: evaporation

B: condensation

C: precipitation

D: collection

2.

a) Path should run through the water cycle on the diagram

b) Pencil path should be a circle

EZ✓

Part C

1.
Group of organisms that live and interact with each other; Examples will vary

2.
1) organisms are similar

2) live in same geographic area; Examples will vary

3.
Yes, ecosystems change; Populations grow, shrink or disappear, species might move in.

4.
Producers able to produce own food, consumers depend on others for food, decomposers break down dead matter to recycle

5.
Helpful: medicine, food
Harmful: bacteria spreading, viruses

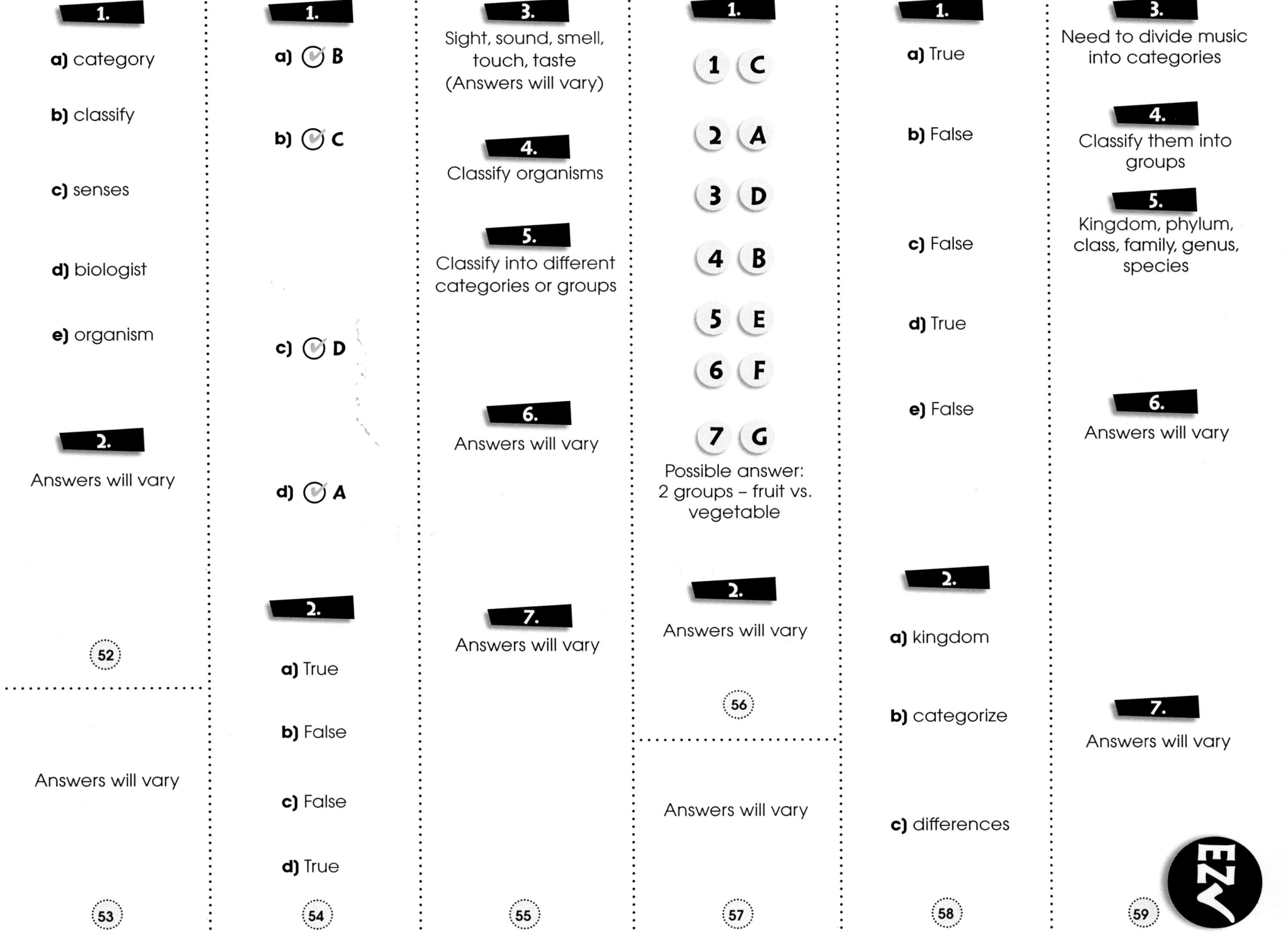

1.

a) category

b) classify

c) senses

d) biologist

e) organism

2.

Answers will vary

52

Answers will vary

53

1.

a) B

b) C

c) D

d) A

2.

a) True

b) False

c) False

d) True

54

3.

Sight, sound, smell, touch, taste (Answers will vary)

4.

Classify organisms

5.

Classify into different categories or groups

6.

Answers will vary

7.

Answers will vary

55

1.

1 C

2 A

3 D

4 B

5 E

6 F

7 G

Possible answer: 2 groups – fruit vs. vegetable

2.

Answers will vary

56

Answers will vary

57

1.

a) True

b) False

c) False

d) True

e) False

2.

a) kingdom

b) categorize

c) differences

58

3.

Need to divide music into categories

4.

Classify them into groups

5.

Kingdom, phylum, class, family, genus, species

6.

Answers will vary

7.

Answers will vary

59

EZ✓

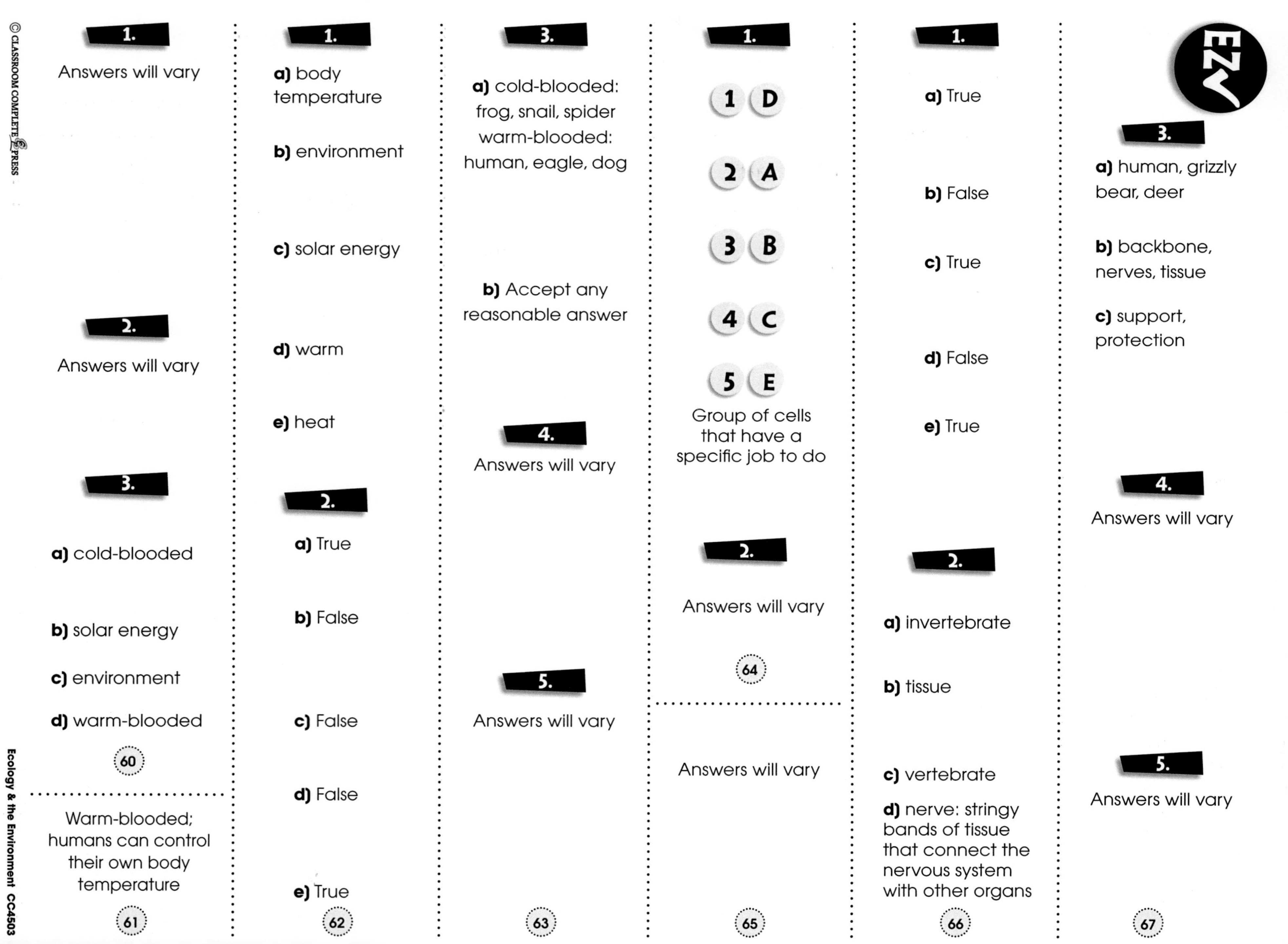

Page 60

1. Answers will vary

2. Answers will vary

3.

a) cold-blooded

b) solar energy

c) environment

d) warm-blooded

Page 61

Warm-blooded; humans can control their own body temperature

Page 62

1.

a) body temperature

b) environment

c) solar energy

d) warm

e) heat

2.

a) True

b) False

c) False

d) False

e) True

Page 63

3.

a) cold-blooded: frog, snail, spider warm-blooded: human, eagle, dog

b) Accept any reasonable answer

4. Answers will vary

5. Answers will vary

Page 64

1.

1 D

2 A

3 B

4 C

5 E Group of cells that have a specific job to do

2. Answers will vary

Page 65

Answers will vary

Page 66

1.

a) True

b) False

c) True

d) False

e) True

2.

a) invertebrate

b) tissue

c) vertebrate

d) nerve: stringy bands of tissue that connect the nervous system with other organs

Page 67

3.

a) human, grizzly bear, deer

b) backbone, nerves, tissue

c) support, protection

4. Answers will vary

5. Answers will vary

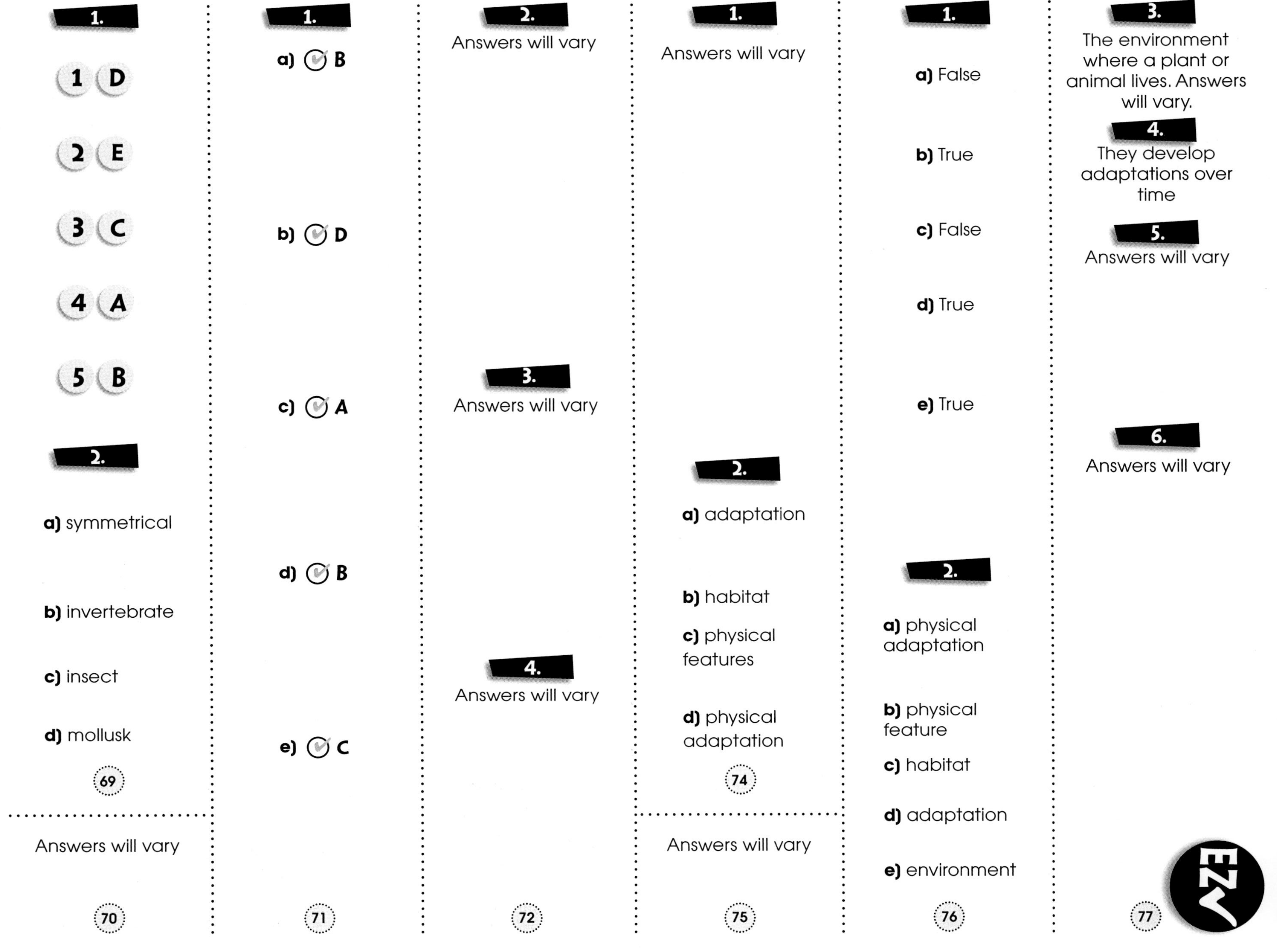

1.

1 D

2 E

3 C

4 A

5 B

2.

a) symmetrical

b) invertebrate

c) insect

d) mollusk

69

Answers will vary

70

1.

a) ✓ B

b) ✓ D

c) ✓ A

d) ✓ B

e) ✓ C

71

2.
Answers will vary

3.
Answers will vary

4.
Answers will vary

72

1.
Answers will vary

2.

a) adaptation

b) habitat

c) physical features

d) physical adaptation

74

Answers will vary

75

1.

a) False

b) True

c) False

d) True

e) True

2.

a) physical adaptation

b) physical feature

c) habitat

d) adaptation

e) environment

76

3.
The environment where a plant or animal lives. Answers will vary.

4.
They develop adaptations over time

5.
Answers will vary

6.
Answers will vary

77

EZ✓

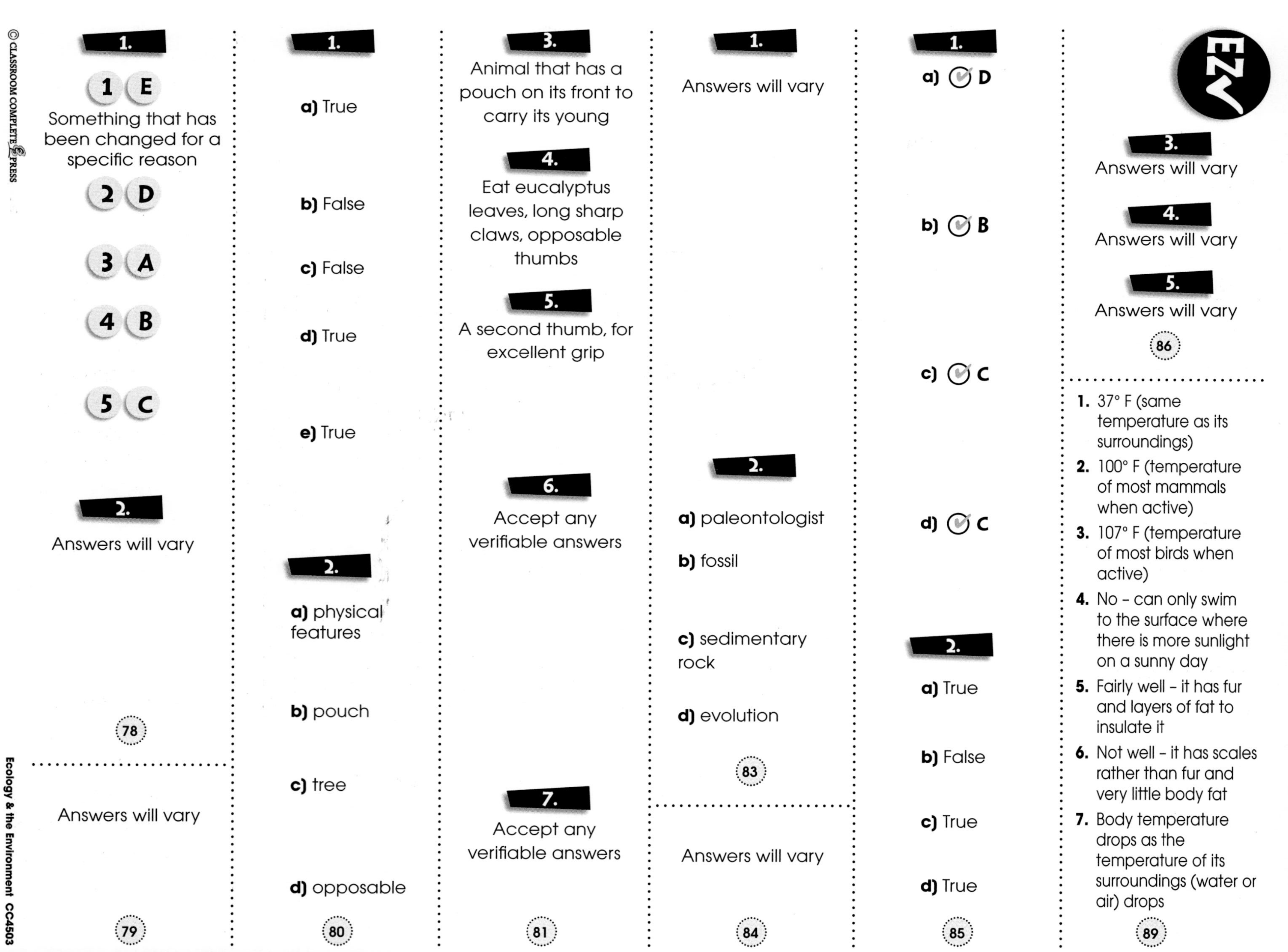

1.

1 E — Something that has been changed for a specific reason

2 D

3 A

4 B

5 C

2.

Answers will vary

(78)

Answers will vary

(79)

1.

a) True

b) False

c) False

d) True

e) True

2.

a) physical features

b) pouch

c) tree

d) opposable

(80)

3.

Animal that has a pouch on its front to carry its young

4.

Eat eucalyptus leaves, long sharp claws, opposable thumbs

5.

A second thumb, for excellent grip

6.

Accept any verifiable answers

7.

Accept any verifiable answers

(81)

1.

Answers will vary

2.

a) paleontologist

b) fossil

c) sedimentary rock

d) evolution

(83)

Answers will vary

(84)

1.

a) ✓ D

b) ✓ B

c) ✓ C

d) ✓ C

2.

a) True

b) False

c) True

d) True

(85)

EZ✓

3.

Answers will vary

4.

Answers will vary

5.

Answers will vary

(86)

1. 37° F (same temperature as its surroundings)
2. 100° F (temperature of most mammals when active)
3. 107° F (temperature of most birds when active)
4. No – can only swim to the surface where there is more sunlight on a sunny day
5. Fairly well – it has fur and layers of fat to insulate it
6. Not well – it has scales rather than fur and very little body fat
7. Body temperature drops as the temperature of its surroundings (water or air) drops

(89)

Word Search Answers

Across:

1. classification
5. biologist
7. warm-blooded
9. species
10. environment
12. paleontologist

Down:

1. cold-blooded
2. symmetrical
3. organism
4. physical adaptation
6. mollusk
8. evolution
11. vertebrate
13. solar
14. fossil

p	c	v	r	f	g	s	e	i	c	e	p	s	w	q	k	o	b
h	w	a	r	m	b	l	o	o	d	e	d	y	s	a	c	p	i
y	e	v	o	l	u	t	i	o	n	n	y	m	d	z	a	p	o
l	w	f	s	w	e	t	l	l	n	v	h	m	n	r	t	o	l
u	d	r	a	u	r	v	x	a	h	i	n	e	e	t	e	s	o
m	v	a	z	m	w	y	u	j	g	r	t	t	r	y	g	a	g
s	e	c	e	g	i	f	h	k	f	o	g	r	v	h	o	b	i
r	r	v	d	f	g	l	m	y	r	n	b	i	e	d	r	l	s
t	t	b	n	m	j	g	y	t	e	m	r	c	w	f	y	e	t
y	e	d	i	n	h	c	a	r	a	e	f	a	d	h	h	f	d
u	b	m	q	s	v	b	m	u	y	n	v	l	x	b	y	r	w
l	r	m	a	z	x	c	v	b	g	t	m	o	d	g	n	i	k
c	a	a	o	r	i	n	v	e	r	t	e	b	r	a	t	e	d
l	t	s	l	l	s	a	s	d	f	g	f	s	h	f	s	n	e
a	e	d	k	e	l	u	w	e	r	t	o	m	a	y	r	f	d
s	h	f	j	d	f	u	p	r	t	y	s	s	b	k	t	m	o
s	e	n	s	e	g	j	s	i	o	u	s	i	i	y	t	e	o
d	f	g	h	j	h	j	k	k	a	l	i	n	t	w	i	y	l
a	d	a	p	t	a	t	i	o	n	l	l	a	a	h	s	q	b
t	c	e	s	n	i	a	s	d	f	g	m	g	t	f	s	e	d
q	w	e	r	t	y	u	l	o	p	l	n	r	f	d	u	w	l
c	l	a	s	s	i	f	i	c	a	t	i	o	n	z	e	b	o
p	a	l	e	o	n	t	o	l	o	g	i	s	t	w	y	p	c

Part A

1. True
2. False
3. True
4. True
5. False
6. True
7. True
8. False

Part B

a) invertebrate

b) vertebrate

c) vertebrate

Part C

1. Warm-blooded can control their own body temperature, cold-blooded cannot

2. Divide things into groups based on similarities. Answers will vary.

3. They have backbones, nerves and tissues.

4. A physical feature that has been changed for survival purposes. Koala: opposable thumb, has long sharp claws, eats eucalyptus leaves

5. The change of populations of living organisms over time. They study fossils.

EZ✓

EZ✓

1.

a) microscope

b) organism

c) magnify

d) building block

e) matter

f) cell

2.

Possible answers:

b) grain of sand

c) one pancake

d) one sheet of paper

e) paper pulp

f) one Lego piece

g) one item in the pile (i.e. shirt)

95

Answers will vary

96

1.

a) True

b) False

c) False

d) True

e) False

2.

a) mass

b) microscope

c) cell

97

3.

Building block of life (smallest unit of living matter)

4.

No – microscope

5.

No – different shapes, sizes, jobs to do

6.

Answers will vary

7.

Answers will vary

98

1.

1 G

2 D

3 F

4 C

5 A

6 B

7 E

2.

Answers will vary

99

Answers will vary

100

Possible answers: Person, potted plant, insect

101

1.

a) C

b) D

c) B

d) B

2.

a) False

b) False

c) True

d) False

102

3.

Single-celled – made up of 1 cell
Multicellular – made up of many cells

4.

Organizes all the activities in the cell

5.

Small structures that help carry out day-to-day operations of the cell

6.

Answers will vary

7.

Answers will vary

103

1.

Answers will vary

2.

a) Cytoplasm

b) organelles

c) Cilia

d) cell membrane

e) nucleus

f) cell

(105)

brain

(106)

1.

a) membrane

b) particles

c) inside

d) paddles

e) ostrich's

2.

a) True

b) False

c) False

d) False

e) True

(107)

3.

Answers will vary

4.

Answers will vary

5.

Answers will vary

(108)

1.

a) multicellular organism

b) specialize

c) nucleus

d) cell specialization

e) cell membrane

f) Cytoplasm

2.

Answers will vary

(109)

Answers will vary

(110)

1.

a) True

b) False

c) False

d) True

e) True

2.

a) nucleus

b) cytoplasm

c) cell specialization

d) cell membrane – outside covering of cell

(111)

3.

a) factory boss

b) front door

c) power source

4.

Answers will vary

5.

Answers will vary

(112)

EZ✓

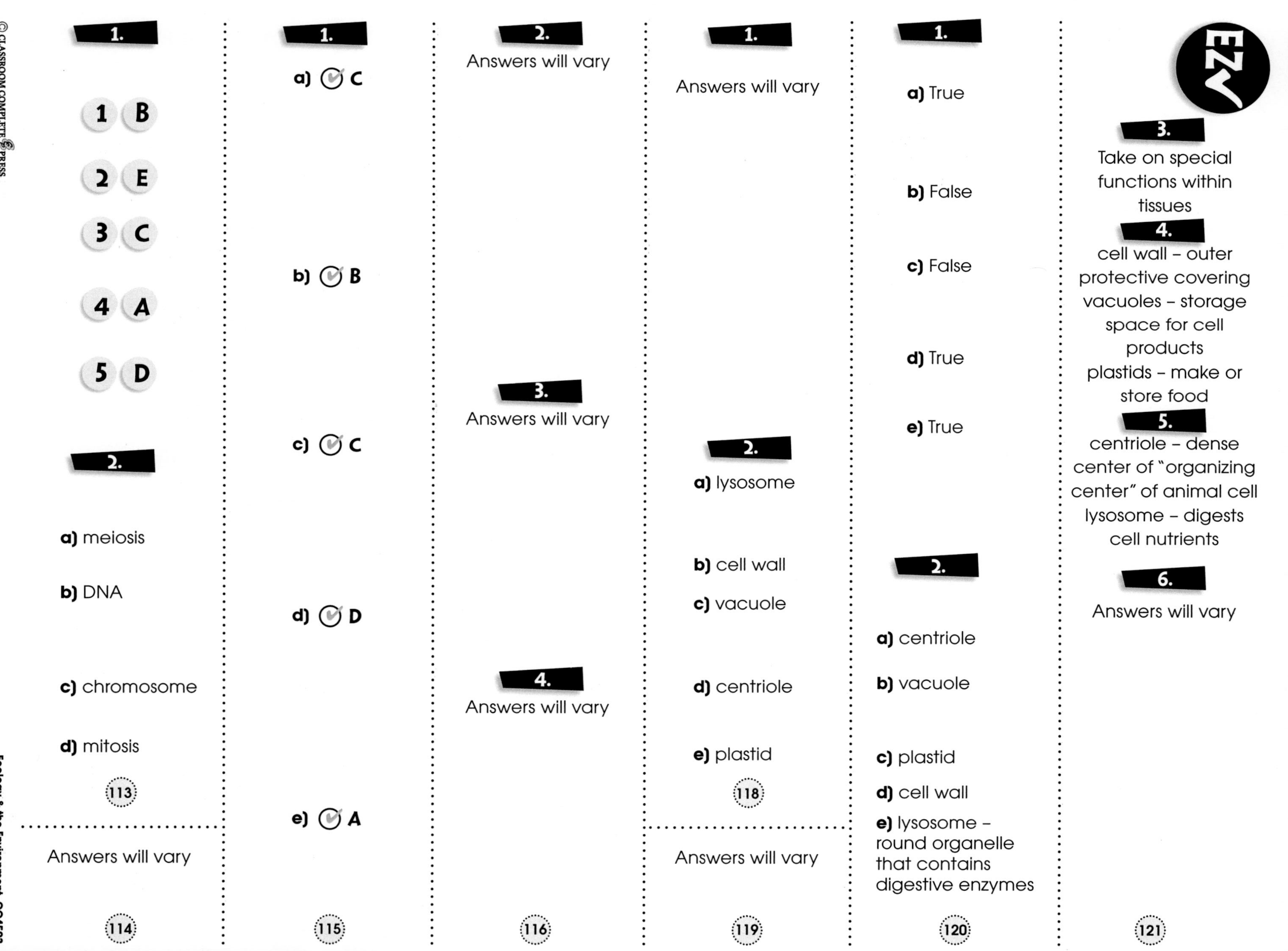

1.

1 B
2 E
3 C
4 A
5 D

2.

a) meiosis

b) DNA

c) chromosome

d) mitosis

(113)

Answers will vary

(114)

1.

a) C

b) B

c) C

d) D

e) A

(115)

2.
Answers will vary

3.
Answers will vary

4.
Answers will vary

(116)

1.
Answers will vary

2.

a) lysosome

b) cell wall

c) vacuole

d) centriole

e) plastid

(118)

Answers will vary

(119)

1.

a) True

b) False

c) False

d) True

e) True

2.

a) centriole

b) vacuole

c) plastid

d) cell wall

e) lysosome – round organelle that contains digestive enzymes

(120)

EZ

3.
Take on special functions within tissues

4.
cell wall – outer protective covering
vacuoles – storage space for cell products
plastids – make or store food

5.
centriole – dense center of "organizing center" of animal cell
lysosome – digests cell nutrients

6.
Answers will vary

(121)

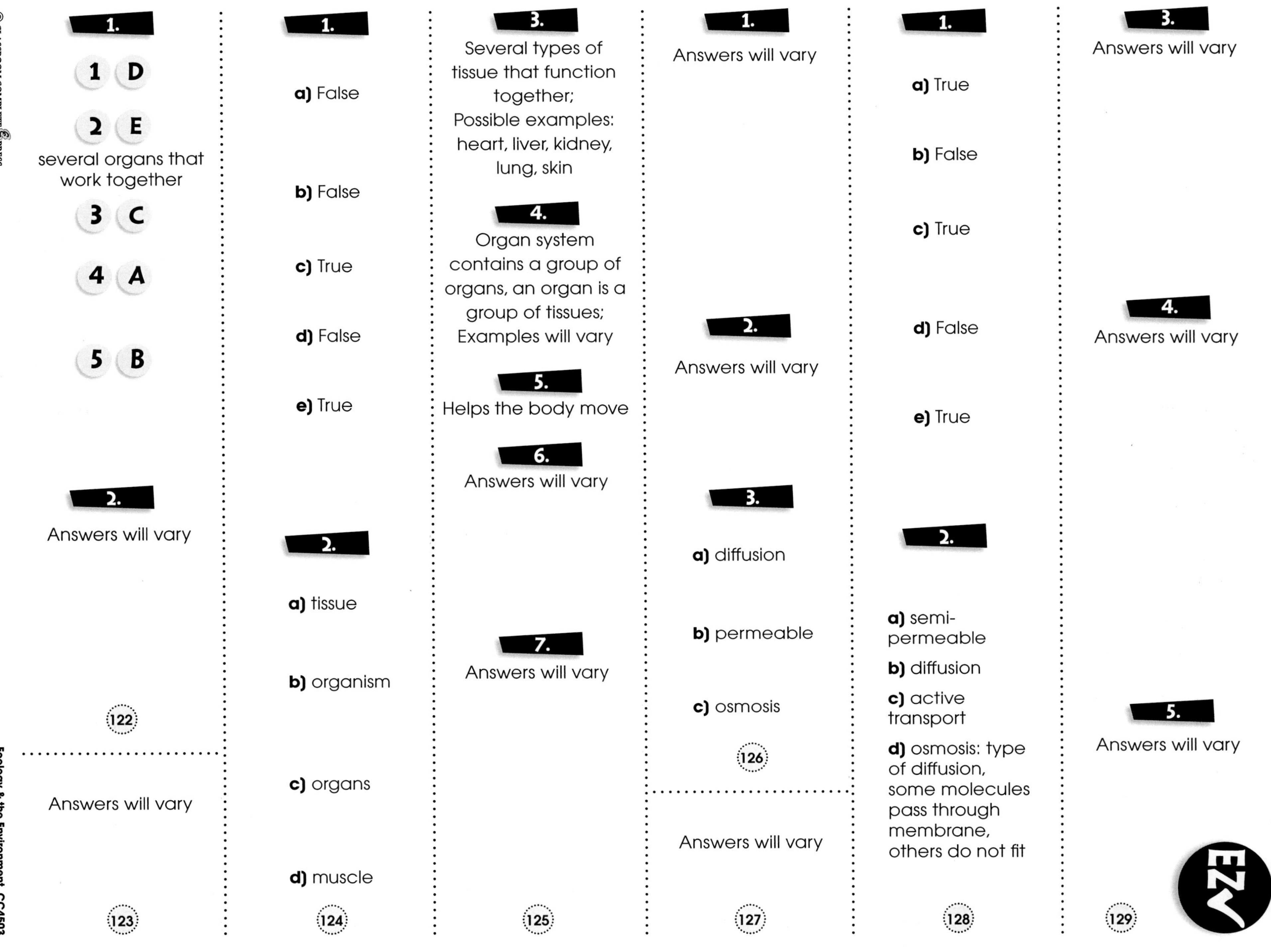

1.

1 D

2 E several organs that work together

3 C

4 A

5 B

2.

Answers will vary

(122)

Answers will vary

(123)

1.

a) False

b) False

c) True

d) False

e) True

2.

a) tissue

b) organism

c) organs

d) muscle

(124)

3.

Several types of tissue that function together;
Possible examples: heart, liver, kidney, lung, skin

4.

Organ system contains a group of organs, an organ is a group of tissues;
Examples will vary

5.

Helps the body move

6.

Answers will vary

7.

Answers will vary

(125)

1.

Answers will vary

2.

Answers will vary

3.

a) diffusion

b) permeable

c) osmosis

(126)

Answers will vary

(127)

1.

a) True

b) False

c) True

d) False

e) True

2.

a) semi-permeable

b) diffusion

c) active transport

d) osmosis: type of diffusion, some molecules pass through membrane, others do not fit

(128)

3.

Answers will vary

4.

Answers will vary

5.

Answers will vary

(129)

EZ✓

Across:

1. osmosis
3. meiosis
6. nucleus
11. cell membrane
12. cell wall
15. chromosome

Down:

1. organ
2. organelle
3. matter
4. organism
5. vacuoles
7. cytoplasm
8. single celled
9. plastid
10. semi permeable
11. cilia
13. mitosis

Word Search Answers

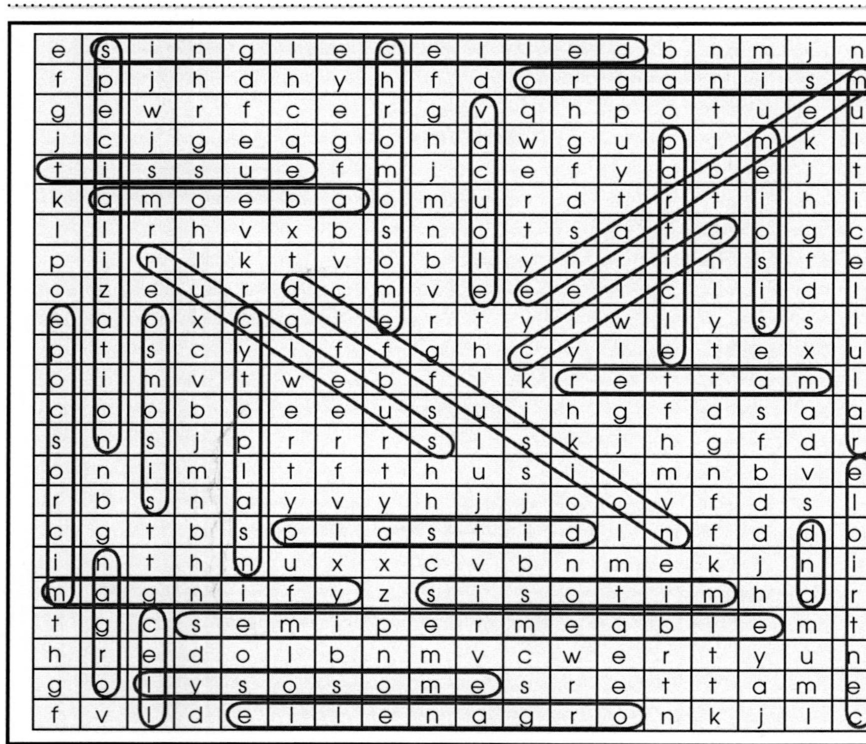

Part A

1. True

2. False

3. False

4. True

5. True

6. False

Part B

A cell membrane

B nucleus

C cytoplasm

EZ✓

Part C

1. Building block of life; microscope

2. Carries genetic information; in nucleus

3. Possible answers: nucleus – controls everything that happens in the cell cell membrane – holds all parts of cell in place cytoplasm – where all the cell's activities take place

4. Yes; meiosis – sexual reproduction (produces sex cells) mitosis – asexual reproduction (no sex cells produced)

5. cell wall – rigid outer covering, vacuoles – large sacs that store proteins, waste, etc., plastids – make and store food

An Ecosystem

Producers, Consumers & Decomposers